Oliver Mayo

Evolution by Natural Selection and Ethics: What in evolution has ethical implications?

 J. Cramer
in Borntraeger Science Publishers

Mayo: Evolution by Natural Selection and Ethics
What in evolution has ethical implications?
Oliver Mayo
Adjunct Professor of Biometry, University of Adelaide, Australia

We would be pleased to receive your comments on the content of this book:
editors@schweizerbart.de

Front cover: Soursob (Oxalis pes-caprae L.), as seen in mediterranean Australia, was once a 'hopeful monster', since it is in fact a sterile pentaploid, unable to set seed. Despite this, it is an extraordinarily successful coloniser, producing a carpet of yellow in Spring over hundreds of thousands of hectares. The pollen-collecting bee, also alien to Australia, is wasting the plant's time, since it cannot pollinate other plants of the one giant clone.

Photo: Oliver Mayo

ISBN 978-3-443-50040-5

Information on this title: www.borntraeger-cramer.com/9783443500405

© 2018 Gebr. Borntraeger Verlagsbuchhandlung, Stuttgart, Germany

Publisher: Gebr. Borntraeger Verlagsbuchhandlung
Johannesstr. 3A, 70176 Stuttgart, Germany
mail@borntraeger-cramer.de
www. borntraeger-cramer.com

∞ Printed on permanent paper conforming to ISO 9706-1994

Typesetting: Da-TeX, Leipzig

Printed in Germany by Online-Druck.biz, Krumbach

Table of contents

What in evolution has ethical implications?

'"Magna est veritas et prævalebit!" Truth is great, certainly, but, considering her greatness, it is curious what a long time she is apt to take about prevailing.' T. H. Huxley

1 Introduction

The writing of this book was inspired or at least initiated by the reading of a short book by Ferdinand Brunetière. Writing in 1894, Brunetière considered the arguments of the previous half-century about the direction of human evolution. He noted that biologists such as T. H. Huxley had established that progress was not a necessary consequence of change occasioned by natural selection, and that, indeed, regression was possible. In Brunetière's eyes, this vindicated the biblical account of the Fall of Man and the doctrine of Original Sin. (A translation of the remarkable work of Brunetière is set out in the Appendix.)

Progress to Brunetière was only moral or spiritual progress; material advance e.g. scientific progress is irrelevant to the argument he made. Yet increased brain size, above some unknown minimum, has probably been necessary for the evolution of a moral sense, as for other 'higher' attributes. We do not know whether other animals possess such a sense. We see them behave as if they possess shame, as we understand it. Two hundred years ago, Jean Paul's character Dr Katzenberger could ask 'Where is the absolute tie between spiritual shame and the valves in the veins which dam up the blood in the cheeks?' (Paul 1809, p. 77) This was to ask 'How?' 'Why?' was much harder. Darwin first assessed 'What?' Blushing was indeed widespread as a mark of human shame, amongst other emotions. He noted that it had been so recognised for thousands of years e.g. in the Talmud (Old Testament). He speculated that it arose from self-attention which interfered with local blood circulation. How it happens is now understood (e.g. Mellander *et al.*, 1982).

Darwin had been dead for two decades when Brunetière wrote his book, but he could well have chosen Huxley as his main source of current evolutionary thinking not just because his work was up to date but because Huxley recognised that evolution by natural selection was not progressive. Darwin, on the other hand, appears always to have held the view, expressed near the end of the Origin of Species (1859, p. 489), that 'all corporeal and mental endowment will tend to progress towards perfection' by means of natural selection. This is not the case, as will be discussed, though any particular adaptation that remains beneficial to an organism will slowly be refined and improved by this means.

It was clear to Brunetière that Man has fallen (e.g. Brunetière par. 5, quoting Calvin 'Original sin is a corruption and hereditary perversity of our nature'). It is not so clear to all believers. Barnes (1924, p. 162–3) wrote: '…the wider teleology, which assumes that in the whole evolutionary process there is purposive action directed to a definite end, is left intact by biological inquiry. We cannot deny that in the evolutionary development of life upon the earth there has been progress, culminating in man; and, by progress, we mean the successive appearance of powers and qualities which we unanimously accept as valuable. We cannot interpret such progress without assuming that it is due to an intelligent Will. It is true that at every stage progress has been largely by environment, and that the whole scheme by which human personality has been evolved seems ultimately dependant on certain properties of inorganic matter.'

De Duve (2009a, 2009b) trod the same path as Brunetière, but informed by his own prodigious contribution to human genetics and understanding of evolutionary biology, and reached much the same conclusions as Brunetière. He went on to formulate a set of 'options for the future' which he viewed as moral imperatives, but still they were informed by revelation.

It seemed worthwhile to try to evaluate, at least qualitatively, what the post-Brunetière century's research on evolution, especially human evolution might permit us to conclude about the interaction of evolution and ethics, in the absence of revelation. I note views to the contrary, e.g. Coyne (2009, p. 245):

> How can you derive meaning, purpose or ethics from evolution? You can't. Evolution is simply a theory about the process and patterns of life's diversification, not a grand philosophical scheme about the meaning of life. It can't tell us what to do, or how we should behave. And this is the big problem for many believers, who want to find in the story of our origins a reason for our existence, and a sense of how to behave.

> Most of us *do* need meaning, purpose and moral guidance in our lives. How do we find them if we accept that evolution is the real story of our lives? That question is outside the domain of science. But evolution can still shed light on whether our morality is constrained by our genetics. If our bodies are the product of evolution, what about our behaviour? Do we carry the psychological baggage of our millions of years on the African savannah? If so, how far can we overcome it?

Some of Coyne's assertions will be addressed in the following pages. As noted above, Brunetière wrote 'science enquires only into the "how" of things, never into the "why"', but this is a 'disastrous error' (pars. 29–30 in Brunetière below).

Coyne's statement that 'Evolution is simply a theory' is curious and warrants brief discussion. Among other things, evolution is an interpretation of observed diversity, of changes in diversity over measured time, of appearances in and disappearances from the fossil record of life forms. Up to a point, it is no more a theory than is a tabulation of the monarchs of France with their dates. Evolution by natural selection is a theory. Evolution by divine creation is a theory. For Brunetière, revelation as set out in the Old Testament of the Bible was not a theory in the same way, since it could not be falsified, only confirmed, or accepted as correct if science disagreed with it. (Some revelations have been falsified, but generally have thereafter been re3interpreted by their adherents.)

I should also say what I am not trying to do. Fain (2008) asks 'Can we prove the law of evolution?' He does not state what 'the' law of evolution is; he appears to accept 'the fact of evolution'. Mayr (1991) said that there were several 'laws of evolution', one of which is that evolution occurs; an interbreeding group of organisms, or species, changes its attributes over time. Extinction is another 'law of evolution': it is the norm, according to the fossil record. Natural selection occurs; we see it in action in our short lifetime. This too is a 'law'. (As Darwin, 1859, p. 469, wrote 'What limit can be put to this power, acting during long ages and rigidly scrutinising the whole constitution, structure, and habits of each creature,— favouring the good and rejecting the bad? I can see no limit to this power, in slowly and beautifully adapting each form to the most complex relations of life.')

Fain's conclusion, following standard Popperian thinking, is that we cannot prove a law; we can only disprove it. Popper, as cited by Fain, accepts the 'laws' of heredity (Mendel's 'laws') and of natural selection (Darwin's 'law', though he did not call it that). Popper further says that the fact of evolution cannot be disproved, because it is one of a kind, the historical record, written in the rocks and the biosphere. There is confusion here; because evolution is inseparably dependent on chance and necessity, prediction is very difficult, there cannot be biological equivalents to the laws of physics: under certain circumstances, certain consequences must always follow. In biology, everything, including the 'laws of evolution' just mentioned, is probabilistic. This is hardly surprising; biology is not physics; psychology is not rocket science; it is much more complicated than that.

Fain states that 'the prevalent opinion is that … natural selection explains all evolution on earth, and that from the moment life was created … we can predict the development of life on earth' (Fain, p. 435). Leaving aside the question of who holds this prevalent opinion (I have never met anyone who does), we see that Fain illustrates the confusion perfectly: we are getting better at explaining what has happened, but this does not mean that we can predict what will happen. To give a simple example, from 1897 onwards it was recorded that insects were evolving resistance to insecticides, and such evolution has happened repeatedly (Forgash 1984). How it would occur in any particular case could not be predicted. In experimental production of insecticide resistance, it has usually arisen through selection of small inherited changes, classically Darwinian, whereas investigation of the genetical basis of insecticide resistance in wild populations has shown that a major gene mutation has been increased greatly in frequency in the resistant populations. Modifiers of deleterious pleiotropic effects of the gene may be selected for over time, but the critical point will have been the selection of a rare mutant of a major gene. The same appears to have happened in human populations living in human populations living near the Atacama Desert in Chile, who have evolved tolerance to high levels of arsenic in the water supply (Apata *et al.*, 2017).

Fain states further that 'we cannot discover … a theory of evolution' (p. 437). It is my contention that we (starting with Darwin) have discovered such a theory, the theory of evolution by natural selection. Fain does not address this theory, indeed gives no evidence that he has read, for example, *The Origin of Species* (Darwin 1859), *The Genetical Theory of Natural Selection* (Fisher 1999) or even *The Ant and the Peacock* (Cronin 1992), and does not appear to accept well-established basic biology, such as the biparental production of offspring by humans ('A complete living organism develops from semen' p. 431).

The reason for Fain's refusal to address evolution by natural selection as investigated by thousands over 150 years is that he opposes his 'theocentric' worldview to a particular 'atheistic-materialistic or secular one' (p. 428). To Brunetière, 'what is *natural*' is precisely 'what is not *human*' (Brunetière below par. 8). I have devoted so much space to this view because I want to make it clear that this disjunction is irrelevant to my goal, which is to see whether evolution (as seen, mostly brought about by natural selection) guides us or perhaps forces us to particular ethical positions.

'Brunetière's book'

Natural selection is a remarkable agent, metaphorically speaking: it appears to be working towards a goal, as Darwin (1859, p. 186) pointed out 'To suppose that the eye with all its inimitable contrivances for adjusting the focus to different distances, for admitting different amounts of light, and for the correction of spherical and chromatic aberration, could have been formed by natural selection, seems, I freely confess, absurd in the highest degree.' However, as has often been explained, the goal is only there in hindsight; small differences in 'perfection' exist, within and between species. In consequence, for natural selection the end justifies the means because there is no end, in the sense of purpose; the means used by natural selection varies according to the raw material at hand: in many respects, the octopus's eye has a better *Bauplan* than our own, for example.

Working for the benefit of the individual organism, natural selection's focus is on the short term, whatever the perfection wrought over time. Scarpino *et al.* (2016) give a fine contemporary example. If workers stay home during an influenza epidemic, often at the behest of their superiors, the epidemic can spread faster than if the afflicted workers stayed at work. While the conclusion is only provisional, it is probably an example that illustrates how local, short-term adaptive behaviour can produced medium-term negative effects. The imperfection of the human organism is likely to have arisen from selection for short-term adaptation that locks evolution into a path that is adaptive but not optimal because of the starting point. As Brunetière wrote: 'we are the present term of an infinite series of animal ancestors' (Brunetière par. 4 below), taking 'infinite' metaphorically, as did Brunetière, who accepted a first cause.

De Duve (2009a p. 163) made the short-term focus of natural selection a key component of our 'genetical original sin', as he saw it. Humans in particular have, in his view, evolved to make excellent short-term judgements that ignore the long-term consequences of chosen actions. This problem will be seen to be implicit in many of the behaviours discussed below, and of course is evident in almost every aspect of reproduction in particular.

I should also say that I shall for the most part not deal with the evolution of behaviours shared widely in the animal kingdom, though I shall use comparison of behaviours where appropriate.

Take, for example, courage. Watching rainbow lorikeets feeding on gum-blossom in an 80 kph wind before a big storm, one sees intuitively where courage comes from: the need to continue a life-sustaining activity in the face of a hostile environment. The birds communicate incessantly as they feed and move about, but there is no need to suppose that they are doing it to keep their spirits up; it is their normal conduct sustained in difficult circumstances. The behaviour has evolved and is basic instinct in action. What needs more explanation at the level with which I am concerned is not a basic instinct itself but the ability to overcome it, Gehlen's 'relief' perhaps (e.g. Delitz, 2011, Chapter 4).

In drawing information from and making comparisons with other species, I therefore do not say that the behaviour in the non-human species is the same, rather that the outcomes are conformable with the human behaviour that has a particular label. An example should make this clear. Darwin (1871/1901, pp. 868–9) wrote

'the musical faculties, which are not wholly deficient in any race, are capable of prompt and high development, for Hottentots and Negroes have become excellent musicians, although in their native countries they rarely practise anything that we should consider music. Schweinfurth, however, was pleased with some of the simple melodies which he heard in the interior of Africa. But there is nothing anomalous in the musical faculties lying dormant in man: some species of birds which never naturally sing, can without much difficulty be taught to do so; thus a house-sparrow has learnt the song of a linnet. As these two species are closely allied, and belong to the order of Insessores, which includes nearly all the singing-birds in the world, it is possible that a progenitor of the sparrow may have been a songster. It is more remarkable that parrots, belonging to a group distinct from the Insessores, and having differently constructed vocal organs, can be taught not only to speak, but to pipe or whistle tunes invented by man, so that they must have some musical capacity. Nevertheless it would be very rash to assume that parrots are descended from some ancient form which was a songster.'

There is no suggestion in this passage that the acquired song of a parrot is serving the same function as song in humans, rather that the different brain and vocal apparatus of a parrot have produced sounds comparable with human song.

In discussing response to natural selection, I shall have frequent recourse to the concept of heritability, that is, the proportion of observed phenotypic variation that is genetically determined i.e. the ratio of genetical variance (V_A or V_G) to total variance in the trait (V_P), variance being a measure of the amount of variation. This can be broad, in including all genetical variation in the denominator, or narrow, in including only additive genetical variation. Additive genetical variation is the variation always exposed to natural selection, partly determining the rate of change under natural selection (from the 'fundamental theorem of natural selection', Fisher 1999). Heritability, as a ratio, does not indicate how much change can be achieved by selection; that depends on V_A, as Fisher (1951) reminded its users. As a tool in human genetics, heritability has many detractors, and is being rendered irrelevant in human genetics by genomics, but it has been very widely used, so estimates for many human behavioural traits are available, and the studies are in most cases remarkably consistent (Polderman et al., 2015).

If we consider a trait fundamental to many others, such as memory, its high heritability (0.4–0.8) is made up of many components, closely linked genetically. Blokland et al. (2011) have examined the architecture of the inheritance of memory, by considering activation of specific regions of the brain. The patterns are complex, and highlight the fact that selection on any trait will bring about correlated responses in other traits. The effect of natural selection for improved memory would be very complex at the level of brain function; correlated response will in general be a limitation on progress under selection and hence to the use of V_A or h^2 to assess possible recent selection or likely future selection. Nevertheless, one must begin somewhere; for an account of the expected effects on evolutionary change of genetic correlation, see Blows and Hoffmann (2005).

Across all traits examined in twin studies over half a century, Polderman et al. found that heritability averages about 0.5, and for two-thirds of traits studied, resemblance between twins in a pair is accounted for by a simple additive model. It might be thought, therefore that mention of heritability is nugatory, since for almost all human traits, variation exists that could bring about substantial change in the trait by natural selection. However, it is still worth noting, because newer methods will allow interpretation in different ways, particularly through detection and estimation of recent selective change.

If heritability is very low, this may mean that there is very little genetical variation (V_A or V_G is very small), or that phenotypic variation is great (V_P is very large). If V_G is very low, this may mean that the trait has been under strong selection e.g. melanin in European populations (Zaidi et al., 2017). That heritability is high and V_P is substantial for a trait suggests lack of strong recent directional selection and perhaps a lack of an extreme optimum for the trait. These are only suggestions; as pointed out by many, e.g. Mayo et al. (1990), even when a trait is strongly associated with fitness, persistent V_A does not mean that there is an intermediate optimum. Single gene differences influence complex traits, and persistent V_A in those traits, as I shall consider in a number of cases, but so many have been elusive, apart from those with major deleterious effects, that they cannot contribute greatly to the argument.

It should be noted that many traits differ between sexes, besides those related to sex per se. Karp et al. (2017) analysed hundreds of traits in mice specifically to determine which were influenced by sex and found that over half the traits were indeed influenced by sex. Their concerns were with potential differential drug response, unexpected because trials were carried out on males only, but the concern is more general than that. In the discussion that follows, I have tried not to draw inferences relevant to sex from such trials. I have also drawn attention in a few of many cases to differences between sexes in the inheritance of traits. The overall arguments should not be influenced by any difference between human sexes.

1.1 The question: What in evolution has ethical implications?

This question has two components. First, can anything in biology have ethical implications; is biology relevant to ethics? Secondly, if the answer to the first question is yes, what evolutionary facts, processes or theories have ethical implications?

The answer to the first question seems to be yes: bringing about a human birth has ethical implications, as discussed below, and so does bringing about a death, or so most societies in recorded history appear to have concluded. Perhaps this conclusion is over-simplified, but it is my starting point.

I also begin by accepting the reality of the 'naturalistic fallacy', as introduced by Hume. It is not universally accepted, so I cover it in a separate section. Brunetière noted that Guyau (1885) had attempted to produce an ethics independent of obligations or duties (or indeed sanctions) but dismissed it in a lengthy footnote, saying 'In France, we love to play with words!' (Brunetière below, par. 1 footnote 2)

Anthropocentrism is a closely related source of error. In this light, Huxley (1894a, p. 48) wrote:

> Suppose, for argument's sake, that all mammals and birds are subjects of pleasure and pain. Then we may be certain that these forms of consciousness were in existence at the beginning of the Mesozoic epoch. From that time forth, pleasure has been distributed without reference to merit, and pain inflicted without reference to demerit, throughout all but a mere fraction of the higher animals. Moreover, the amount and the severity of the pain, no less than the variety and acuteness of the pleasure, have increased with every advance in the scale of evolution. As suffering came into the world, not in consequence of a fall, but of a rise, in the scale of being, so every further rise has brought more suffering. As the evidence stands, it would appear that the sort of brain which characterises the highest mammals and which, so far as we know, is the indispensable condition of the highest sensibility, did not come into existence before the Tertiary epoch. The primordial anthropoid was probably, in this respect, on much the same footing as his pithecoid kin. Like them, he stood upon his 'natural rights,' gratified all his desires to the best of his ability, and was as incapable of either right or wrong doing as they. It would be as absurd as in their case, to regard his pleasures, any more than theirs, as moral rewards, and his pains, any more than theirs, as moral punishments.

At the same time, I accept the idea that some ideas may be inconceivable. As Haldane (1928, p. 286) put it, 'Now, my own suspicion is that the universe is not only queerer than we suppose, but queerer than we can suppose. I have read and heard many attempts at a systematic account of it, from materialism and theosophy to the Christian system or that of Kant, and I have always felt that they were much too simple. I suspect that there are more things in heaven and earth than are dreamed of, or can be dreamed of, in any philosophy. That is the reason why I have no philosophy myself, and must be my excuse for dreaming.' A simple example comes from beautiful work on the representation of space and time in the brain. It appears that the hippocampus, which is basic to memory in humans (Scoville and Milner 1957), contains 'time cells' and 'place cells', so named because of identified activities, which 'represent the spatial and temporal relationships of distant stimuli in order to support learning of these relationships' (Howard and Eichenbaum 2014). If learning with regard to space and time takes place relatively early and establishes a framework within which a person operates, this may explain how it comes about that Newtonian absolute space seems natural, commonsensical, whereas Einsteinian absolute space-time does not. (When it comes to uncommon events, common sense, of course, is not to be trusted as Goethe trusted it: '…art and science, independently of philosophy, and by means of a free action of natural human powers, have always thriven best. … I have always kept myself free from philosophy. The common-sense point of view [is] also mine [as with Schubart]'. Goethe, 1850 p. 121)

Quantum theory also takes us away from the everyday. Cubitt *et al.* (2015) have suggested that certain properties of matter will always remain undecidable, indeterminable: unknowable facts. This is against all our ideas of being able to interrogate nature and learn her properties.

Nature should be conceived broadly, as Shakespeare makes Polyxenes say to Perdita in *The Winter's Tale* (and as noted by Lankester, 1907, p. 3):

> You see, sweet maid, we marry/A gentle scion to the wildest stock; /And make conceive a bark of baser kind/By bud of nobler race; this is an art/Which doth mend nature, – change it, rather: but/The art itself is nature.

What is natural includes *Medea* by Euripides. Anyone privileged to see Helen McRory play the title role at the National Theatre in London will have been struck by the play's, the director's, the actor's attempt to make the audience understand infanticide, at least in some sense. I saw the production in August 2014, and later in the same year learnt with horror of an apparent multiple infanticide in Queensland. Somehow the play had made the mother's position less alien yet more distressing.

Here is R. A. Fisher on feticide, which in his context included infanticide:

> … what had seemed patriotic and high-minded to Plato and Aristotle, a venial offence and a fashionable folly to Pliny and Seneca, was anathematized as a damnable sin by the Christian fathers, such as Tertullian, and was made a capital offence in the laws of Valentinian.

> Since the change in moral opinion with respect to feticide, together with associated changes in sexual morality, took place over a period during which the ancient world experienced the religious revolution of conversion to Christianity, and since these concurrent changes were ultimately connected causally, it is important to avoid the misapprehension that the change in moral feeling, with which we are concerned, was derived as a consequence from the acceptance on Christian doctrine. It would, I believe, be a fundamental mistake to imagine that the moral attitude of any religious community is to any important extent deducible from the intellectual conceptions of their theology (however much preachers make it their business so to deduce it), and still more to suppose that official doctrine is not itself largely moulded by the state of the popular conscience. The facts available to guide us in the present case are:

(i.) The progressive change of moral opinion among pagan writers from Plato to the jurist Julius Paulus, who about the beginning of the third century AD, stated the opinion that the exposure of children was morally, though not legally, equivalent to murder, and expressed strong disapproval to the practice of feticide. The opinion of these writers, who either knew nothing of Christianity, or rejected its *doctrine, cannot easily be ascribed to the state of Christian feeling upon the* subject.

1.1 The question: What in evolution has ethical implications?

13

(ii.) Our earliest authentic source of Christian doctrine, the story as told in the Gospels, teaches an attitude of gentleness, forbearance and self-sacrifice which has ever since been regarded as ideally Christian. It contains, however, no condemnation of feticide; and cannot even be regarded as the source of the theological doctrine of the damnation of unbaptised infants, even if born dead, which undoubtedly at a later date exerted an important influence in crystallizing Christian opinion upon this subject. It cannot easily be argued that, while not specifically condemning feticide, the gentle and humane character of the Gospel teaching in reality determined the later attitude of the church, for there is nothing gentle or humane in the doctrine we have quoted, and the early Christian legislation against sexual offences certainly seems to err on the side of excessive ferocity. On a statute of Constantine Gibbon remarks:

The successful ravisher was punished with death; and as if simple death were inadequate to the enormity of his guilt he was either burnt alive, or torn in pieces by wild beasts in the amphitheatre. The virgin's declaration that she had been carried away with her own consent, instead of saving her lover, exposed her to share his fate. The slaves, whether male or female, who were convicted of having been accessory to the rape or seduction, were burnt alive or put to death by the ingenious torture of pouring down their throats a quantity of molten lead.

We can understand the temper of such legislation as the work of men filled with a temperamental fear and loathing of sexual licence, working in a frenzy of fanatical enthusiasm; we cannot explain it as the work of broad-minded and tolerant men convinced by the Gospel story of the divinity of Jesus.

(iii.) That a stricter sexual morality, involving a more vehement condemnation of feticide, did in fact characterize Christian as opposed to Pagan ethics, when these are contrasted contemporaneously, must be ascribed in large part to the direct appeal made by Christianity to the sanction of the individual conscience, which made it the more responsive to popular feeling, even when latent and unexpressed. This effect was certainly enhanced by the solicitude of the early Church for persons of the meanest occupational status, since ... the evolutionary effects of variations in reproduction are greatest in the lowest social class.

Fisher considered that these changes reflected social evolution of the conscience, but also thought that natural selection was involved. In an earlier paper (Fisher 1922, p. 193), he suggested that natural selection for 'moral instincts' which resist the 'temptation to infanticide' had been 'severe' in 'civilised' people. Fisher did not mention the possible deleterious effects on a society practising infanticide, e.g. on the reproduction rate, which could have led to its abandonment for pragmatic reasons described as moral. Nor did he mention the prohibition of slavery in Western society which took place over a few centuries, ending in the 19th, with no evidence to the outside observer of natural selection associated with the social selection for more humane practices. (Other statements in the passage can be contested, of course: I quote the passage because it describes an actual change in ethics over a relatively short period: the moral standing of infanticide. Some might say that attitudes to feticide have changed again over the last century in many different societies.)

Fisher followed Darwin in trying to explain the evolution of human behaviour by natural selection. Looking back at Darwin's pioneering attempts, which I discuss further below (section 2.2 and later), Daiches Raphael (1958) wrote 'psychologists do not try to use natural selection as the medium whereby the moral faculties have developed. They have instead constructed theories of ... how conscience is built up from other mental endowments, such as love and fear, in response to the stimuli of family and wider social environment.' Rapid change in moral sentiments, such as the attitude to feticide, is thus explained in environmental terms, but of course this does not alter the fact that the whole complex has been subject to natural selection, and the assumed fundamental traits 'such as love and fear' will also have evolved by natural selection. (Indeed, from Huxley onwards, according to Guyau (1885), many have regarded conscience as an epiphenomenon, i.e. an emergent property arising from other properties.)

Whatever may have been the case in any genetical contribution towards the tendency to abhor feticide, it could be argued that directional natural selection must greatly reduce normal variation in traits where the optimum is at one end of a scale. For example, there is very little non-deleterious genetical variation in many meristic characters. Most humans have one head, one heart, one liver, one copulatory contrivance, two eyes, two ears, two arms, two legs, and so on. Indeed, there is modest genetical variation in lateral asymmetry in general (e.g. Tsujino and Takahashi 2012, Rao *et al.*, 2002).

In a similar way, sensory perception might be expected to be directionally selected. Keenness of eyesight, sensitivity of smell: is there a limit to the advantage of more and more precise sensation? Following others (see section 2.3 below), I shall argue against any such limits. Much variation in the senses is deleterious. The sense of smell, less important for survival in humans than in some other mammals, reveals non-deleterious loss of function in many specificities (Amoore 1967, Buck 2004, Guillot 1948).

2 General considerations

All of the properties of the human organism will have been influenced through our evolution by natural selection, except perhaps for the soul, if dualism is correct. (The evidence for dualism is still lacking, so I shall not mention it again.) Accordingly, where a topic is mentioned, that is in this general consideration or as an example of a trait that may provide guidance on how to find a biological basis for ethics, may seem to be arbitrary. However, some topics will recur or are methodological in nature, so they are dealt with in this part.

2.1 Consciousness

Possession of a conscience appears to require consciousness. The *Oxford English Dictionary* defines consciousness as follows: 'the state of being aware of and responsive to one's surroundings; a person's awareness or perception of something; the fact of awareness by the mind of itself and the world'. The third meaning is the one of interest in evolutionary terms, since it invites well-known questions: what is consciousness in biological terms? Do all sentient beings possess consciousness? Is consciousness the same in man and other animals? How did consciousness evolve?

If the answers to the second and third questions were affirmative, this might have the implication that treatment of other sentient beings different from treatment of other human beings might require ethical justification. However, this would again be deriving 'ought' from 'is'.

Consciousness as we understand it requires self-reflection, or recursion of some kind. Was this present before language evolved? If so, how were ideas about it shared, if they were indeed shared?

In contrast to consciousness is sleep. It has long been understood what sleep's purpose is, speaking teleologically. Shakespeare listed its properties: it 'knits up the ravelled sleeve of care ...' In the same way, we have always had clear ideas about dreaming, part of sleep. Feltham wrote, not long after Shakespeare, 'Dreams are notable means of discovering our own inclinations. The wise man learns to know himself by the night's black mantle, as by the searching beams of day. In sleep, we have the naked and natural thoughts of our souls: outward objects interpose not, either to shuffle in occasional cogitations, or hale out the included fancy' (in Makower and Blackwell 1912, p. 13). Browne added 'dreams may be fallacious concerning outward events, yet may they be truly significant at home; and whereby we may more sensibly understand ourselves' (in Makower and Blackwell 1912, p. 19). Many subsequent thinkers have espoused views on the nature and meaning of dreams, usually on the basis of personal experience and interaction.

Aspects of sleeping behaviour are highly heritable, e.g. Partinen *et al.* (1983) estimated the heritability of both sleep duration and sleep quality (self-rated) as 0.44. Sehgal and Mignot (2011) reviewed many studies that identified specific gene loci associated with sleep disorders, hence likely to influence the nature of normal sleep. More directly relevant, sleep characterised by rapid eye movements (REM sleep), during which dreaming occurs, is very strongly influenced by genetics (Adamczyk *et al.*, 2015), so that one can conclude that the occurrence of dreaming, if not the content, is genetically influenced. What is important in the present context is whether the will is free in sleep. It is by definition not the conscious will that is ruling; is behaviour in sleep therefore certainly driven by something else within the person?

2.2 Belief

I accept the act of faith inherent in conducting scientific activity, including thought. This idea goes back at least to Jacobi, in the late 18th century (Watson, 2011, p. 147), and was well stated by Huxley (1894c, p. 243):

> It is quite true that the ground of every one of our actions, and the validity of all our reasonings, rest upon the great act of faith, which leads us to take the experience of the past as a safe guide in our dealings with the present and the future. From the nature of ratiocination, it is obvious, that the axioms, on which it is based, cannot be demonstrated by ratiocination. It is also a trite observation that, in the business of life, we constantly take the most serious actions upon evidence of an utterly insignificant character. But it is surely plain that faith is not necessarily entitled to dispense with ratiocination just because ratiocination cannot dispense with faith as a starting-point; and that because we are often obliged, by the pressure of events, to act on very bad evidence, it does not follow that it is proper to act on such evidence when the pressure is absent.

The belief that the universe is orderly and that its rules can be discovered through careful, accurate, honest observation, experimentation and theory-building has the implication that the person engaged in such investigation needs to be careful, accurate and honest in such investigations. Since much of the universe, from black holes to the clotting cascade, is not easy for an individual to investigate as a sole practitioner, it follows that the researcher must engage carefully, accurately and honestly in dealing with collaborators, editors, funding bodies and all others on whom the

researcher's activities impinge. Thus, right conduct emerges as a necessity in 'work-related' activities; Babbage (1830) set out the consequences of failure to act rightly in a way that has not been improved to this day. However, this necessity arises from the basic belief rather than from the science itself. Furthermore, it could be argued that there is no necessity for right conduct away from work. Waddington (1941) considered that the ethos implicit in this right conduct provided a basis for a belief system better than those competing at the time he wrote, and he may have been correct, but he did not demonstrate the necessity; his preferred system was one in contention, no more.

This belief system has evolved. It is perhaps only 300 years old (e.g. Keynes, 1946). Lankester (1907, p. 7) states it quite strongly: 'Man is held to be a part of nature, a product of the definitive and orderly evolution which is universal; a being resulting from and driven by the one great nexus of mechanism which we call Nature. He stands alone, face to face with that relentless mechanism. It is his destiny to understand and to control it.' With reservations in regard to the role of chance and the possibility of understanding everything, this is the outlook that has driven much discovery. Whitehead (1926/1938, p. 83) put the belief system less positively: 'The world of science has always remained perfectly satisfied with its peculiar abstractions. They work, and that is sufficient for it.'

This belief system is different from some others. As Darwin (1871/1901, p. 936) wrote:

> The belief in God has often been advanced as not only the greatest, but also the most complete of all the distinctions between man and the lower animals. It is however impossible, as we have seen, to maintain that this belief is innate of instinctive in man. On the other hand a belief in all-pervading spiritual agencies seems to be universal; and apparently follows from a considerable advance in man's reason, and from a still greater advance in his faculties of imagination, curiosity and wonder. I am aware

that the assumed instinctive belief in God has been used by many persons as an argument for His existence. But this is a rash argument, as we should thus be compelled to believe in the existence of many cruel and malignant spirits, only a little more powerful than man; for the belief in them is far more general than in a beneficent Deity. The idea of a universal and beneficent Creator does not seem to arise in the mind of man, until he has been elevated by long-continued culture.

Indeed, Darwin (1871/1901, p. 149) held very strongly that this second belief system had itself evolved:

… any animal whatever, endowed with well-marked social instincts, the parental and filial affections being here included, would inevitably acquire a moral sense or conscience, as soon as its intellectual powers had become as well, or nearly as well developed, as in man. For, firstly, the social instincts lead an animal to take pleasure in the society of its fellows, to feel a certain amount of sympathy with them, and to perform various services for them. The services may be of a definite and evidently instinctive nature; or there may only be a wish and readiness, as with most of the higher social animals, to aide their fellows in certain general ways. But these feelings and services are by no means extended to all the individuals of the same species, only to those of the same association. Secondly, as soon as the mental faculties had become highly developed, images of all past actions and motives would be incessantly passing through the brains of each individual; and that feeling of dissatisfaction, or even misery, which invariably results, as we shall hereafter see, from any unsatisfied instinct, would arise, as often as it was perceived that the enduring and always present social instinct had yielded to some other instinct, at the time stronger,

but neither enduring in its nature, nor leaving behind it a very vivid impression. It is clear that many instinctive desires, such as that of hunger, are in their nature of short duration; and after being satisfied, are not readily or vividly recalled. Thirdly, after the power of language had been acquired, and the wishes of the community could be expressed, the common opinion how each member ought to act for the public good, would naturally become in a paramount degree the guide to action. But it should be borne in mind that however great weight we may attribute to public opinion, our regard for the approbation and disapprobation of our fellows depends on sympathy, which, as we shall see, forms an essential part of the social instinct, and is indeed its foundation-stone. Lastly, habit in the individual would ultimately play a very important part in guiding the conduct of each member; for the social instinct, together with sympathy, is, like any other instinct, greatly strengthened by habit, and so consequently would be obedience to the wishes and judgement of the community.

Whitehead (1926/1938) and many others have described how religion and science have co-evolved; both have changed, though in general revelation has not changed and scientific knowledge has. Scientific faith, that is, the belief that the universe works to rules that can be understood, should also be distinguished from other faiths that invoke the name of science. 'The sole method open to mankind by which he can improve his lot is an increasing mastery of nature. In the degree only of our scientific knowledge is there any hope of release from the material fetters which still weigh upon the vast majority of men. That assumption, of course, itself rests upon a faith. It believes in the power of knowledge …' (Laski, 1944, p. 38) Concealed in this statement is an acceptance not just of Bacon's dictum but of the perfectibility of humans, which Brunetière knew was an illusion.

Thomas Henry Huxley (1825–1895), Darwin's friend and defender, was Brunetière's main source of -up-to-date evolutionary theory in the 1890s. Huxley was also significant in reintroducing the Scottish philosopher David Hume's ideas (e.g. Section 2.4) to the general public. (Image of T. H. Huxley; frontispiece of vol. 2 of Leonard Huxley 1900 Life and Letters of Thomas Henry Huxley. London, Macmillan. The image in the book is taken from the portrait by J. Collier in the National Portrait Gallery in London).

2.3 Discrimination

Discrimination is a part of the processes of observation, perception and decision-making, whether by an amoeba following a molecular concentration gradient towards a food source or a banker assessing the creditworthiness of a potential customer. The senses appear to have evolved to become more precise, given the range of defective mutants that make them less precise; through loss of the less effective forms, the outcome has been greater precision.

Duncan and Sheppard (1963) have shown how sensory discrimination could become more precise, through repeated testing, and that such discrimination appears to be continuous, not quantal, there being in principle no lower limit to its precision above the level of the individual photon or electron. In their words,

The continuous or discontinuous nature of sensitivity is of considerable evolutionary importance, as Fisher (1999) pointed out. If differences, however small, can be detected on a statistical basis, not only by man but by other animals, then in situations where an animal is exerting selection on another, by virtue of its ability to discriminate between individuals of different phenotypes, as a predator might in mimicry, a change, however small, in the animal being selected, will not be selectively neutral (Fisher 1999).

Much newer work demonstrates the validity of the concept of continuity as put forward by Duncan and Sheppard (e.g. Dotsch *et al.* 2016). This same question applies, of course, to plants' and micro-organisms' interactions with their environments. It is broader than sensory perception. Mathesius and her colleagues (e.g. Hassan and Mathesius 2012, Ferguson and Mathesius 2014) are showing how phytohormone contributions from host plants and soil microbes (especially bacteria) affect fitness of host and symbiont or parasitic microbes.

More important in the case of animals, perhaps, is the implication that the sensory apparatus itself will be selected continually for minute improvements; discrimination may be expected to become continually finer, unless selection pressure is eased. There is a further implication: when choice is forced between very similar possibilities, the probability of error in a single test rises towards 0.5 as the necessary discrimination becomes finer. If the difference is, say, one part in a million between the objects under test, any single choice is essentially random, or biassed by personal preference.

2.4 The naturalistic fallacy

As noted above, I accept the reality of the 'naturalistic fallacy', as introduced by Hume:

In every system of morality, which I have hitherto met with, I have always remark'd, that the author proceeds for some time in the ordinary ways of reasoning, and establishes the being of a God, or makes observations concerning human affairs; when all of a sudden I am surpriz'd to find, that instead of the usual copulations of propositions, is, and is not, I meet with no proposition that is not connected with an ought, or an ought

not. This change is imperceptible; but is however, of the last consequence. For as this ought, or ought not, expresses some new relation or affirmation, 'tis necessary that it shou'd be observ'd and explain'd; and at the same time that a reason should be given; for what seems altogether inconceivable, how this new relation can be a deduction from others, which are entirely different from it.

The leap "it is, therefore it should be" is a step too far for many, including me. There are so many counter-examples that it cannot be accepted universally, but more important, one "it" may contradict another "it": competition and co-operation, for example.

To see how misapplication of lessons learned from biology works, consider Lankester's (1907, p. 12) example: an 'objectionable misinterpretation of the naturalists' doctrine of the survival of the fittest in the struggle for existence is that made by journalists and literary politicians, who declare, according to their political bias, either that science rightly teaches that the gross quality measured by wealth and strength alone can survive and should therefore alone be cultivated, or that science (and especially Darwinism) has done serious injury to the progress of mankind by authorizing this teaching.'

A watered-down version of the fallacious principle, "it is, therefore we should be guided by it", still contains an imperative, but can perhaps be followed in some respects.

My unoriginal stance is not universally accepted; Rozzi (1999, p. 914) wrote "...a full account of the interrelationships between science and ethics needs to go not only from is to ought but from ought to is". As an example, Rozzi argues, like earlier writers, that knowledge of the kinship of all living creatures should lead to changes in agency: 'live and let live' to vegetarianism, for example. Kinship supports the "intrinsic value of nonhuman life" (p. 917). Knowledge of evolution by natural selection should eliminate any force in the idea of anthropocentrism (p. 918).

Hall (2011, p. 158) has written:

> ...I have shown that many of the criteria signifying moral considerability *can* be located in the plant kingdom. Close observation of plant life-history demonstrates that plants are communicative, relational beings – beings that influence and are influenced by their environment. They also reveal that plants have their own purposes, intricately connected with finding food and producing offspring. Like other living beings, plants attempt to maintain their own integrity in changing environmental conditions. Plants display intelligent behaviour in order to maximise both their growth and the production of offspring.
>
> Despite these findings, I do not wish to argue for moral considerability based upon provable criteria. A drawback with approaches that attempt to *prove* moral considerability is that they struggle with the infamous gulf between questions of fact and the impetus for moral action, the "is-ought" gap identified by David Hume. Within the Western ethical framework, the fact that a plant or animal has interests or intrinsic value does not automatically require those intrinsic values to be respected. This is a well recognized gap between a factual description of a being's attributes and the need to subscribe to an ethics that takes these into consideration.

It is not just 'intrinsic value' or 'the Western ethical framework' (is there just one?); it is logic. As Hume put it (*Treatise of Human Nature* IV, p. 44, cited by Huxley, 1894d, p. 156) "Whatever is intelligible and can be distinctly conceived, implies no contradiction, and can never be proved false by any demonstration, argument, or abstract reasoning *a priori*." But Hall's argument is convincing on other grounds, as will be discussed elsewhere; here I simply note the importance, for me, of not deriving "is" from "ought".

Changeux (2008) has proposed an interesting path round the fallacy. He seeks an authentic 'science of the normative' which integrates these different aspects of the problem into an evolutionary and neuro-cultural context. From the development of sympathy, in particular, and the ability to put oneself in another's place, Changeux considers that systems of values, while not unchangeable, result over time in 'normative crystallizations' whereby normative systems are internalised, so that 'what ought to be' becomes part of 'what is'. 'My idea here is that, in the transition from monkeys to humans, cognitive functions, in particular consciousness and artistic activity, are associated with a major development of cerebral organisation which manifests itself particularly by the expansion of the cerebral cortex and, more especially, of the prefrontal, parietotemporal and cingulate neocortex, in a tight relation with the limbic system' (Changeux, p. 100). Earlier (p. 57), he wrote 'the normative process would correspond to a progressive consolidation of the moral rules and would be the result of repeated experiences of approval and disapproval on the basis of sympathy.' Then 'normative crystallizations' are a part of the human brain; conscience is part of consciousness. The question of whether 'is' can yield 'ought' becomes redundant.

If Changeux's argument has any validity, then any ethical lesson that may be drawn from evolved behaviour could become the basis for ethics drawn from evolution.

Harris (2010, p. 25) is in no doubt that the naturalistic fallacy is not a meaningful concept in attempting to relate ethics to real life: 'If we define 'good' as that which supports well-being, as I suppose we must, the regress initiated by Moore's 'open question argument' really does stop. While I agree with Moore that it is reasonable to wonder whether maximising pleasure in any given instance is 'good', it makes no sense at all to ask whether maximising well-being is 'good'. It seems clear that what we are really asking when we wonder whether a certain state of pleasure is 'good', is whether it is conducive to, or obstructive of, some deeper form of well-being.' Harris does not define well-being formally, but adopts a starting 'premise that it is good to avoid behaving in such a way as to produce the worst possible misery for everyone.' (Harris, op. cit., pp. 58–9), Indeed, everyone ought to be able to able to agree with it, provided that it is not interpreted in the sense of Genesis 1 28 ('And God blessed them, and God said unto them, Be fruitful, and multiply, and replenish the earth, and subdue it: and have dominion over the fish of the sea, and over the fowl of the air, and over every living thing that moveth upon the earth.'). However, it is still a postulate or axiom, not something induced from the facts of nature. Harris (op. cit., pp. 250–1) cites Daniel Dennett's (Dennett, 1995, p. 468) argument by assertion: 'If 'ought' cannot be derived from 'is', just what *can* it be derived from? ... ethics must be *somehow* based on an appreciation of human nature – on a sense of what a human being is or might be, and on what a human being might want to have or want to be. If *that* is naturalism, then naturalism is no fallacy.' The point is once more that an axiom is needed in order to relate ethics and the natural world. (Some might say that this is to assume what needs to be proved, but provided that the axiom is stated clearly, and that the inference, e.g. co-operation generally promotes well-being and hence is to be encouraged, is clearly related to the assumption, I do not think that the reasoning is circular.)

2.5 Axiomatic grounding for ethics

Let us consider a special case: rape. The axiom is that rape is ethically unacceptable, bad, or evil. Thornhill and Palmer (2000) tacitly accept this axiom, because they ask, and answer, the question 'why humans have not been able to put an end to rape'. They answer, first, the reasons for rape are not understood (more fundamentally, 'most people lack any understanding of the ultimate (that is, evolutionary) causes of why humans are the way they are'), and secondly, '[f]or

25 years, attempts to prevent rape have not only failed to be informed by an evolutionary approach; they have been based on explanations designed to make ideological statements rather than to be consistent with scientific knowledge of human behavior' Thornhill and Palmer (2000, p. 2).

Questions automatically arise. Is current human scientific knowledge sufficient for confident application to a major, seemingly perpetual unacceptable act (crime, sin)? Thornhill and Palmer propose to develop an approach to the prevention of rape based on knowledge of evolution by natural selection. If we substitute 'murder' for 'rape' in argument, do we see a realistic proposal? While rape is a vicious act, combining mental and physical cruelty, intimacy and violence, and so particularly vile, murder is also a dreadful act. Does the fact that it need not be intimate (consider only the drone pilot, the sniper, the poisoner) make it qualitatively different from rape? Can any crime, sin or antisocial behaviour be abolished by understanding its origins and building prevention thereon?

Let us accept, for the moment, that rape is a special case, as a perversion of the natural generative and pleasure-giving act. Thornhill and Palmer argue that, just as there are special adaptations relating to physical coercion to enable copulation in other species (e.g. certain insects), so there could be special male psychological adaptations leading to rape. They do not adduce evidence for this proposition and in addition do not exclude the possibility that male behaviour leading to rape is not something that has been specifically influenced by natural selection, but is an outcome of a range of other factors (aggression, size, parental investment in procreation and child rearing etc.) that have been directly influenced by natural selection, especially that component identified as sexual selection. They also note many male human behaviours are 'clearly' by-products of well-identified and validated features of human sexual behaviour (op. cit., p. 60).

Violence by men towards women is widespread in many cultures, but Thornhill and Palmer consider that rape should be seen primarily as a sexual act rather than as a violent act, a 'phylogenetic holdover', given that rape and male violence towards females are found in all great apes (op. cit., pp. 55–6). Sexual selection is involved, given that it is a way 'to circumvent female choice', and female choice is a central contributor to sexual selection (op. cit., p. 53).

In assessing the effects of rape, Thornhill and Palmer write '…we believe that rape is a more traumatic experience [than being beaten], and we maintain that this is because throughout evolution being raped led to the additional negative future consequences of being fertilised by undesired males' (op. cit., p. 59). For males, however, rape is an adaptation that increases male reproductive success by … increasing mate number' (op. cit., p. 59).

They argue that identification of rape as a behaviour that has evolved by natural selection will lead to better means of reducing its incidence.

First, they discount the possibility of using 'positive eugenics' as a means both because of its slowness and because of pleiotropy amongst the genes influencing male sexual behaviour. There are, of course, other reasons for rejecting eugenics as an approach, even when we find that dysgenic selection may be occurring, as in the case of educational attainment in Iceland (Kong *et al.*, 2017).

They suggest that education is necessary, but must be based on the idea that 'men who rape are sexually motivated' (op. cit., p. 93), not on ideas of rape as primarily concerned with violence or control. Furthermore, they argue, the idea that rape is a learned behaviour is incorrect and hence not a good basis for education against rape (p. 140). They do not discuss the possibility that society should change, and that education might lead in this direction, though the abolition of slavery in many societies, the ending of capital punishment in some, the change in regard to infanticide in some

Mediterranean countries over 1500 years ago (already considered in section 1.1 above) and changing attitudes to abortion in the 20th century (see section 3.15) are examples of societal change without genetical change.

In the context of large social changes such as those just mentioned, a major conclusion appears flawed: '*the evolved psychological adaptations that produce male sexual motivation are necessary proximate causes of rape*. It follows that creating environmental conditions that will decrease the frequency of rape requires identification of the exact nature of the psychological mechanisms that guide male sexual behaviour.' Certainly such identification might help to effect change, but society can change without complete knowledge of causation. It should not be complacent to imagine that the incidence of child molestation by Catholic priests this century will be much lower than it was last century, for example.

Thornhill and Palmer's suggestions for how to prevent rape are modest, and do not in the main show much linkage to the evolutionary argument. Education and child-rearing should be informed by better understanding of male and female sexual behaviour, society should be more open, and incarceration of young rapists should be lengthy. Drug treatment is discussed, as dealing with some aspects of the biology, and is not rejected as a possibility.

These questions need to be addressed fully and openly, and both prevention and punishment should be informed as well as possible. However, the conclusion relevant to my enquiry is that this particular axiom-based pursuit of a severe ethical problem has not advanced the likelihood that worthwhile ethical conclusions can readily be drawn from the study of the effects of natural selection.

I am aware that Thornhill and Palmer's thesis was criticised strongly for its first appearance (e.g. Araji, 2000; Hansen, 2001; Wolfthal, 2001), but I have been concerned with the process of trying to build ethics on natural selection, rather than with all the other shortcomings or indeed any merits of their work.

2.6 Natural selection, including sexual selection

Natural selection is central to all of the arguments presented here, and has already been discussed at some length. In the previous section, a flawed understanding of some of the evidence for natural selection was seen to lead to a flawed attempt to build a biological basis for some aspects of ethical behaviour.

Brunetière accepted much of Darwin's argument for evolution by natural selection, though he referred to the *Origin* and a major work by Haeckel as 'novels', because of how little had, in his eyes, been actually proven (par. 36 below). Insofar as anything depended on genetics, he had much right on his side; indeed, as Fisher (1999) explained most clearly, following early English critics, evolution by natural selection was not compatible with Darwin's own erroneous theory of inheritance. However, in the subsequent century the reality of change under natural selection and of speciation has been amply demonstrated, as has the dependence of evolutionary change on inheritance through RNA and DNA.

Natural selection needs to be carefully defined, so as to be sure one id discussing a natural process, not a metaphor: the *Oxford English Dictionary* has 'The process whereby organisms better adapted to their environment tend to survive and produce more offspring'. Leaving aside the slight circularity between adaptation and survival, natural selection is clearly a set of processes in which some aspect of the environment brings about enhanced reproduction by some members of a breeding population as against other members.

Because the environment interacts with organisms, evolution by natural selection must change the environment as experienced by the organism. Fisher (1999, p. 41 *et seq.*) appears to have been the first to note that from the organism's perspective the environment must constantly deteriorate. As a species becomes more successful in dealing with predators, for example, it may be expected to become more

numerous, and hence more individuals of one species will compete for the same resources, making the environment more demanding. On occasion, for example in colonisation of a new environment, this may not be a limitation, but it will generally be true. Similarly, it may be that some members of a species may do better than others, indeed at the expense of others, as seems to be the case in most human societies, but this does not invalidate the rule.

'Nature' is not herself or itself to be understood as an agent, merely a convenient agglomeration of all relevant factors. Mate choice is one such factor, and here the mate choosing a breeding partner is clearly an agent. It is not a moral agent.

Darwin (1871/1901, p. 319, p. 321) distinguished natural selection from sexual selection:

> With animals which have their sexes separated, the males necessarily differ from the females in their organs of reproduction; and these are the primary sexual characters. But the sexes often differ in what Hunter has called secondary sexual characters, which are not directly connected with the act of reproduction; for instance, the male possesses certain organs of sense or locomotion, of which the female is quite destitute, or has them more highly-developed, in order that he may readily find or reach her; or again the male has special organs of prehension for holding her securely.
>
> …
>
> We are, however, here concerned only with sexual selection. This depends on the advantage which certain individuals have over others of the same sex and species solely in respect of reproduction. When, as in the cases above mentioned, the two sexes differ in structure in relation to different habits of life, they have no doubt been modified through natural selection, and by inheritance, limited to one and the same sex. So

again the primary sexual organs, and those for nourishing or protecting the young, come under the same influence; for those individuals which generated or nourished their offspring best, would leave, ceteris paribus, the greatest number to inherit their superiority; whilst those which generated or nourished their offspring badly, would leave but few to inherit their weaker powers. As the male has to find the female, he requires organs of sense and locomotion, but if these organs are necessary for the other purposes of life, as is generally the case, they will have been developed through natural selection. When the male has found the female, he sometimes absolutely requires prehensile organs to hold her; thus Dr. Wallace informs me that the males of certain moths cannot unite with the females if their tarsi or feet are broken. The males of many oceanic crustaceans, when adult, have their legs and antennae modified in an extraordinary manner for the prehension of the female; hence we may suspect that it is because these animals are washed about by the waves of the open sea, that they require these organs in order to propagate their kind, and if so, their development has been the result of ordinary or natural selection. Some animals extremely low in the scale have been modified for this same purpose; thus the males of certain parasitic worms, when fully grown, have the lower surface of the terminal part of their bodies roughened like a rasp, and with this they coil round and permanently hold the females.

The blue-tongued lizard (*Tiliqua scincoides*) has adapted well to Australian suburban gardens but is easily killed by motor vehicles, and may well become extinct in urban regions.

In the century and a half since Darwin's pioneering work, the validity of his hypothesis has been well sustained. It provides a mechanism for the evolution of sexual dimorphism, especially secondary sexual characteristics, the latter being Darwin's focus. Evidence is widespread. Sexual selection can also interact with other forms of natural selection, being itself of course a particular type of natural selection. For example, Zaidi *et al.* (2017) found evidence of local adaptation of human nose shape to climate (width of the nares was influenced by temperature and absolute humidity) but considered that sexual selection might also have had an effect.

Evolution by natural selection as a body of theory has grown but is still recognisably Darwinian. A range of other evolutionary theories (orthogenesis, Lamarckism, creative evolution, mutationism; see Levit *et al.* 2008 for review) has been developed over the past two centuries, but though controversy generated by their proponents has occasionally shed light on evolution, they have not stood the test of time. They will only be referred to where absolutely necessary.

As already noted (section 1), many traits differ between sexes in mammals. This is not relevant to our overall argument, except where interaction among the sexes has ethical implications. These differences among the sexes have also been demonstrated, for the most part, for relatively simple traits, especially in the work of Karp *et al.* (2017) cited earlier and related studies. Speculation has a much older history. For example, Guyau (1885, chapter 4), whose work was important to Brunetière, considered that love of beauty would be selected for, as well as the beauty itself, through sexual selection. It is hard to separate these ideas, though selection against asymmetry may be a part of what has happened.

2.6.1 Utility

Most non-theological approaches to ethics consider something like utility, in that basic principles relate to avoidance of harm to others and provision of pleasure, however defined, to the self. Although Harris (op. cit. pp. 266–272) rejects utility maximisation as an approach, it is very close to his maximising of well-being as a goal. Utility is what is generally improved in evolution by natural selection; it is adaptation.

We see the outcome of natural selection as improved adaptation, which generally comes about through interaction between an organism and its environment. The precise details will in most cases be very hard to ascertain, because they are past history, imperfectly recorded in the genome. Lorenz (1965b, pp. 25–6) wrote:

> A young swift reared in a narrow cave in which it cannot extend its wings (far less beat them up and down), in which it cannot attain a sharp retinal image as the farthest point of the cave is much nearer than its shortest focussing distance, and in which it cannot gain any experience on parallactic shifting of retinal images, nevertheless proves to be perfectly able on the very moment it leaves the nest cavity to assess distances by the parallactic shift of the object's images. It can also cope, in its rapid flight, with the intricacies of air resistance, upcurrents, turbulence and air pockets and can 'recognise' and catch prey, and finally effect a precise landing in a suitable place. The information implicitly contained in the adaptive moulding of all these forms of behaviour to the environmental givens to which they indubitably do fit would fill many volumes. The description of the innate distance computers alone would contain whole textbooks of stereometry and that of the responses and activities of flying, an equal number of data on aerodynamics.

Leaving aside the rhetorical flourishes, we can see in Lorenz's description an assumption of evolutionary optimization of behaviour by natural selection that must be based on the utility to the organism of adaptation. The fact that we can see it in other organisms does not necessarily mean that it is built into our conduct, only into our evolutionary history.

Bentham began his study of utility:

> Nature has placed mankind under the governance of two sovereign masters,

pain and pleasure. They alone point out what we ought to do and determine what we shall do; the standard of right and wrong, and the chain of causes and effects, are both fastened to their throne. They govern us in all we do, all we say, all we think; every effort we can make to throw off our subjection ·to pain and pleasure will only serve to demonstrate and confirm it. A man may claim to reject their rule but in reality he will remain subject to it. The principle of utility recognises this subjection, and makes it the basis of a system that aims to have the edifice of happiness built by the hands of reason and of law. Systems that try to question it deal in sounds instead of sense, in caprice [i.e. whim] instead of reason, in darkness instead of light.

The principle he stated as follows, in 1789:

…the principle that approves or disapproves of every action according to the tendency it appears to have to increase or lessen—i.e. to promote or oppose—the happiness of the person or group whose interest is in question." "By 'utility' is meant the property of something whereby it tends to produce benefit, advantage, pleasure, good, or happiness (all equivalent in the present case) or (this being the same thing) to prevent the happening of mischief, pain, evil or unhappiness to the party whose interest is considered. If that party is the community in general, then the happiness of the community; if it be a particular individual, then the happiness of that individual.

In 1822, Bentham suggested an additional formulation of his principle:

This label has recently been joined or replaced by the greatest happiness principle. This is an abbreviated version of The principle stating that the greatest happiness of all those whose interests are involved is the right and proper—and

the only right and proper and universally desirable—end of human action; of human action in every situation, and in particular in the situation of functionaries exercising the powers of Government. (Chapter 1)

How is happiness defined?

It has been shown that the happiness of the individuals of whom a community is composed, i.e. their pleasures and their security, is the only goal that the legislator ought to have in view; and insofar as legislation affects how individuals behave, the legislator should aim to have their behaviour conform to this same standard. But there is nothing by which a man can ultimately be made to do something, whatever its goal is, except pain or pleasure. Having taken a general view of these two grand objects (namely pleasure and—what comes to the same thing—immunity from pain) in their role as final causes, we now have to take a view of pleasure and pain in their role as efficient causes or means. (Chapter 3)

Any obligations that come out of this approach are essentially part of human society. We can look to determine whether other organisms maximise utility, but this will not present us with an obligation. Precise physiological understanding of mechanisms of the experience of pain and its relationship to other attributes such as anxiety (e.g. Aissouni *et al.* 2017) are unlikely to alter this conclusion.

2.6.2 Optimization

Do organisms maximise their utility, or optimise their state? Do they seek to optimise their state? Do they seek to optimise their happiness?

It is clear that natural selection can improve almost any trait. Resistance of sheep blowflies *Lucilia cuprina* to diazinon poisoning is a very good example. 'The substitution of a pesticide resistant allele (R) at a locus previously fixed for a susceptible allele (S) influences the biochemical and physiological processes associated with development' (McKenzie and Game, 1987, p. 371). Initially, the resistant homozygote is selectively inferior to the other two genotypes in the absence of the pesticide, as may the resistant heterozygote be to the susceptible homozygote. However, independent modifiers of the phenotypes determined by the R/S locus may be segregating in the population under attack from pesticides, and in this case such modifiers may be co-selected with the R allele, thereby improving the fitness of the genotypes containing the R allele. That this is the case with resistance to diazinon was shown by McKenzie & Game: a dominant allele of the modifier gene altered the time of development from egg to adult, in such a way as to enhance the fitness of the animals containing the R allele, in the diazinon-containing environment.

What is noteworthy is that diazinon resistance was determined by a variant of a gene (an allele) that in the absence of diazinon lowered the fitness of its carrier. The effect of natural selection was to increase fitness in the diazinon-containing environment, while lowering it in the absence of diazinon. Optimization began to occur once the frequency of the R allele was high enough for selection of the modifier to be effective. Optimization occurred at the level of the population in the changed environment. There was a cost in the generation of diazinon resistance, but it has to be compared with the opportunity cost of the population dying out, as discussed by Bishop *et al.* (1977) in the case of warfarin resistance in rats, where the 'resistance gene' has many different effects (Rost *et al.* 2004).

Male green treefrogs *Hyla cinerea* solicit females by making a characteristic call. This is difficult in large aggregations of frogs, where much noise is generated. Höbel (2014) found that 'the temporal structure of noise (i.e. duration of noise and silent gap segments) had a stronger effect on male calling behaviour than the spectral composition [of the noise]'. If such

a situation persisted over many generations, selection might be expected both for increased sensory acuity and for increased responsiveness to the nature of the noise. Geographical variation in this behaviour might suggest that such selection has occurred, but habitat reduction and other factors could have been important. Overall, optimization of all traits should not be expected.

Overall, improvement and refinement of a trait do not necessarily mean that it can be optimized. The idea that optimization is not possible in biology is not new; Brunetière (1913, pp. 32–3), quoting an unnamed judge of the French court of appeal, wrote 'Liberty, equality, fraternity; … the three sets of ideas that these words evoke seem in manifest contradiction with the natural laws which rule the evolution of man and societies. How to reconcile liberty with determinism? Equality with the selection which is based on inherent or acquired inequality? Fraternity with the struggle for existence?' He might have added that liberty and equality were in conflict, as Guyau (1885) proposed. The three profound ideals of the French revolution can only be 'satisficed', as Simon (1956) put it.

Huxley (1893, p. 304 *et seq.*) dealt well with the essential inequality of humans, on account of biological differences, since its opposite had been brought into politics by Rousseau and others as an essential property of humans: 'So long as men are men and society is society, human equality will be a dream; and the assumption that it does exist is as untrue in fact as it sets the mark of impracticability on every theory of what ought to be, which starts from it.' (p. 305). This does not mean that attempts to redress inequality and to provide equality of opportunity, for example in access to education and to health care, are to be rejected or dismissed as impossible. It does mean that they are not direct imperatives derived from the properties of evolution by natural selection.

Maximisation of reproductive fitness is what natural selection tends towards. Only rarely will this lead to an indefinite increase in number of offspring; some intermediate optimum is likely to exist. However, human offspring numbers are greatly influenced by social factors, and this has led some (e.g. Vining 1986) to conclude that the disparity in some societies between social success and reproductive success is a challenge to evolution by natural selection as integrated in sociobiology. That many aggregated populations at the national level are not currently breeding sufficiently to replace themselves is seen as another challenge to the ideas of optimisation and maximisation. To the contrary, they simply suggest that what is happening in the present day is not typical of the 300,000 years of the existence of *Homo sapiens*. Evolution by natural selection is how we reached our present state, not a guide to the future, in either an ethical or a biological sense. Galton's duty to breed well (Edwards, 1993, p. 89) is not a biological lesson.

2.7 Inference from historical and model evidence

Most of the discussion of the evolution of ethics depends on present-day organisms, on modelling or on historical data such as the fossil record. Such evidence can rarely provide direct information about behaviour in prehistoric times. Bipedal hominin footprints that showed walking and running might be an example, the way teeth are worn down by use another. Indirect evidence can be close: which of the 'early birds' like *Archaeopteryx* could fly, for example? Physical and computer modelling of fossil data, as well as examination of each new fossil, can answer this question (Foth *et al.* 2014).

When genes involved in important evolutionary changes are identified (e.g. Forkhead box protein P2 (FOXP2) in speech, Lai *et al.*, 2001; Enard *et al.*, 2002), these can perhaps be examined in hominin fossils and present-day primates to infer the timing of changes. For a complex trait like speech, the timing of all the changes will be a matter of indirect inference; see also the brief discussion of Chomsky's single mutation theory below.

For a complex mental trait like sympathy, which appears to leave no marks on the possessor's skeleton, our ability to make inferences is even more distanced from what happened in pre-history. Single gene changes that affect behaviour are well known, though mostly through their manifestation in deleterious phenotypes (e.g. Lesch-Nyhan syndrome, Catel and Schmidt 1959, Lesch and Nyhan 1964). Here again, we are not close to the epigenetic architecture of the set of perhaps simpler traits comprising sympathy. Much of the analysis of the inheritance of behavioural traits relates to five – openness, conscientiousness, extroversion, agreeableness, neuroticism – that are widely taken to describe 'what someone is like', and they are all complex as well as value-laden. They all have heritability of 0.4–0.6 (e.g. Hahn *et al.* 2016).

As noted, most of our evidence is of three kinds: models of what might happen on a certain hypothesis; genetical influences on behaviour in other species that can be the subject of experimentation; and comparative studies of behaviour in humans and other animals. I shall draw on all three, as well, of course, as on evidence of human quantitative inheritance of behavioural traits.

It is worth considering what genetical modelling can and cannot do.

It can show that a system works, in the sense of providing a minimal subset of hypotheses to describe certain behaviour. For example, Feldman and Eshel (1982) developed a precise two locus genetical model to examine the spread of 'selfish' alleles in a genetically 'altruistic' population. They showed that, with complete linkage between the gene affecting 'altruism' and another determining parental 'interference', the development of 'selfishness' may be prevented. Furthermore, they suggested that 'interference' may allow the development of 'altruism' in a 'selfish' population. These results were obtained deterministically i.e. in the equivalent of an infinite population. Mayo and Leach (1985) showed that such evolutionary changes were not certain, indeed might be very unlikely, to occur in small populations. In addition, they showed that it was probably impossible to build a single-locus model with the required properties, but that close linkage of the kind posited by Feldman and Eshel was essential.

As well as population size, Feldman and Eshel had to ignore family size distribution, overlapping generations, environmental variation and pleiotropy of the two hypothetical genes. (An overdispersed family size distribution, which is not unusual in human populations (e.g. Mayo *et al.*, 1973), would make the model unstable.) This is not to criticise the model, which answered a question of interest at the time, merely to note the extreme limitations of a successful model.

Diaz Heijtz *et al.* (2011) have shown that behaviour is influenced by an animal's own microbiota, affecting what look like basic emotions such as anxiety, or other species' analogues of human anxiety. (This is true of many species e.g. zebrafish *Danio rerio*, Davis *et al.* 2016.) There is almost no limit to the factors that can influence behavioural outcomes and the evolution of behaviour; models can be made more complex, but to answer simply posed questions, they must be simple at bottom. If we were actually assessing Feldman and Eshel's 'interference' in real organisms, we would need to consider the web of behavioural traits that would be simultaneously undergoing natural selection. Variants of a single enzyme might influence 'interference', but pleiotropy is the norm, and should in principle never be ignored.

3 Examples

In choosing examples, I am not seeking completeness in coverage of behaviour, nor finality in terms of inferences. I simply want to ensure that sufficient different examples test the ideas inherent in attempting to draw ethical rules from the theory of evolution by natural selection.

3.1 Ageing

Death is a necessary part of life; if organisms had no age-limit, then, barring loss from accident, minor or catastrophic, the globe would be subject to instability and crashes in populations of many different animal species. Death does not imply ageing: there are species that do not appear to age, though most multicellular organisms that have been closely studied manifest ageing.

Ageing is universal in animals, but not uniform. For example, Giraldo *et al.* (2016) found no sensorimotor decline with age in the workers of the social ant *Pheidole dentata*. They found that 'brain functions supporting olfaction and motor coordination' were 'independent of age', a very different result from what has been found in humans, for example.

Medawar (1946) provided the first explanation of ageing in long-lived multicellular organisms such as ourselves: natural selection will favour biological mechanisms that postpone genetically caused damage until reproduction and nurture of offspring are complete. Presbyopia, baldness and loss of hair pigment may be visible examples in humans. A second possibility is 'antagonistic pleiotropy', that is the effects of genes with beneficial effects early in life and deleterious effects late in life. As Charlesworth

(2000, p. 30) summarised our understanding 'senescence is an evolutionary response to the diminishing effectiveness of selection with age [which] explains many aspects of the comparative biology of senescence'.

Death can be programmed, as in the case of various members of the marsupial genus *Antechinus*, in which case ageing is a property of semelparity, and has the appearance of a trait which may advance the cause of the species but which is certainly deleterious to the individual. In this species, the males devote so much energy to mating in their one breeding season that they die 'of exhaustion' afterwards. This may be compared to the mantis species in which the female eats the head of her sexual partner during or immediately after copulation: from the point of an individual male, it is hardly a happy outcome, though perhaps a happy ending. Semelparity is a life pattern that has evolved in few species. A reasonable inference is that it is a hazardous path for a taxon to take. However, this does not mean that such a species is necessarily headed for more rapid extinction than a similar species with unsynchronised reproduction. What is, however, clear is that major habitat disruption is a huge threat for the semelparous species. In this sense, human interference in the environment threatens all other species but those depending on an environment that fluctuates within particular narrow limits may become extinct rapidly.

Kontis *et al.* (2017) have analysed current trends in life expectancy, and have shown that in the OECD and other relatively high-income countries it should reach 90, for both females and males, within 50 years, in the absence of global catastrophes. With this will come a large increase in age-related morbidity, including much dementia, even though diagnosis, in the case of Alzheimer's disease, is steadily improving, as is the quantitation of the genetical component in its causation (Van Cauwenberghe et al., 2016). Kontis *et al.* (2017) conclude that 'rising life expectancy necessitates policies that can support healthy ageing, reframing of education-work-retirement practices, and investment in health and social care', a conclusion built on utilitarian ethics although it is formulated as driven by biology. Park *et al.* (2015) demonstrated that poor environment is associated with decreased telomere length. The end components of chromosomes, telomeres have been established to be good markers of cellular function and cumulative organismal stress: the longer the telomere, the better. These authors conclude that they have 'shown the importance of integrating research on social processes related to health and cellular ageing.' In both papers, the conclusions follow Hume's expectation (section 2.4).

None of these changes alter the present inevitability of death, though they are and will be throwing up many other ethical problems. Does something inevitable have implications for ethics, in the absence of religion? The urge to 'fill the unforgiving minute with sixty seconds' worth of distance run' (Kipling, 1910) is perhaps the outcome of awareness of mortality but the genetics of a sense of urgency (related to anxiety) is not suggestive of any ethical component.

3.2 Altruism

Altruism, already mentioned briefly in connexion with the limitations of modelling, is defined in the *Oxford English Dictionary* as 'Disinterested and selfless concern for the well-being of others' and in zoology as 'Behaviour of an animal that benefits another at its own expense'. The problem that needs to be explained is how it comes about that an organism will do something that is to its own disadvantage. Free will is a concept that is hard to avoid in this context, but will be left till later.

Darwin thought deeply about the subject. To a correspondent, he wrote (Darwin 1903–5, p. 52):

> My conviction as yet remains, that a man who (for instance) jumps into a river to save a life without a second's reflection (either from an innate tendency or from one gained by habit) is deservedly more honoured than a man who acts deliberately and is conscious, for however short a time, that the risk and sacrifice give him some inward satisfaction.

This points the distinction clearly: in the former case (bearing in mind Darwin's defective theory of inheritance and consequent blurring of nature and nurture), generous-spirited behaviour has evolved and is resorted to without conscious thought, whereas in the latter case a conscious decision 'to do the right thing' is involved.

Robinson (2010, p. 60) wrote:

> Altruism has been and still is an issue because Darwinist evolutionary theory has considered it to be one. Why would altruism persist as a trait, when evolution would necessarily select against the conferring of benefit to another at cost to oneself? Hamilton's rule is thought to have resolved the issue by the power of cost-benefit analysis. A scenario involving the rescue of a drowning child demonstrates, without the slightest reference to anything that has happened or might happen in the real world, that a parent would be likely to rescue a child of his own, since that child is presumably the bearer of half his parent's genetic inheritance.

In Robinson's view, there is nothing to explain, because we could cite the New Testament (*Matthew* 25: 35–36): "[Suppose we quote] I was hungry and you fed me, I was naked and you clothed me- but if we did, then we would have proposed a sufficient account of altruism, making Hamilton's equation entirely unnecessary." This is true if we are happy to assume what others wish to investigate and explain. Not everyone wishes to remain in this happy state; one might have hoped that revelation would inspire one to seek knowledge rather than ignorance. It should be emphasised that I always take explanation at the level of mechanism; when Brunetière (par. 6 below) complains that 'the phenomena of life [are not really explained by] by *the properties of organised matter*', he is seeking a 'higher' level of explanation: why the properties of organised matter are as they are. This may be addressed by revelation, but not by science.

> I am not for one moment denying the validity of religious revelation for those rare and special persons who find in an experience private to themselves a reality which transcends the reality in which ordinary men and women share. ... I am arguing the very different thesis that a religious experience based on the claim that it is valid when tested by the canons of scientific evidence, and, because so tested, is entitled to assume the form of an ecclesiastical organisation which may exact the allegiance of mankind, that such experience has no longer any validity for our age. To the degree that we look to such experience as the means of elevating collective well-being, we are giving our confidence to a method which is bound, sooner or later, to fail.

So wrote Laski (1944, p. 101), but while the first part of the argument states the case for the validity of personal revelation to the person who has the experience, the latter part asserts that revelation will always be an operational failure in practice: this is not proven. The implicit point that one person's revelation should not be forced upon another is taken for granted; yet it is this point which is necessary for the rejection of 'is implies ought'.

Mechanisms for the evolution of altruism were first suggested not by Hamilton but by Fisher (1914):

Suppose, for example, that a group of distinguished families possess potential or actual versatility to the extent of being able successfully to fill the role, either of a landed gentleman administering his estates, or of a soldier. A is the eldest son, and stays at home; his brother B goes to the wars; then so long as A has some eight children, it does not matter, genetically, if B gets killed, or dies childless, there will be nephews to fill his place.

Fisher clearly calculated that eight nieces and nephews contained A's genome, on average, ignoring sex determination, the mechanism of which was unclear at the time. A prisoner of his time in some ways, he also ignored females in his calculation.

Hamilton (1964a, b) introduced a general rule for the increase in frequency for a gene which induced its carrier to confer a benefit, β, on a related individual at some cost, γ, to itself. Such a 'gene for altruism' would increase in frequency if $\gamma/\beta < \rho$, where ρ is the degree of relationship between the two individuals. For siblings, $\rho = \frac{1}{2}$. (The usage 'gene for trait X' is widespread shorthand for a gene that influences the propensity to exhibit trait X, but is misleading and often erroneous and will be avoided wherever possible.)

The mechanism requires understanding of the degree of relatedness of different individuals. Speed and Balding (2015) provide a recent review of the precision with which relatedness can be measured. I do not suggest that calculations of relatedness come consciously into altruistic behaviour; recognition or not of a relationship might generally be a key to action. Darwin's warm-hearted view that natural altruism is what has evolved is supported by a recent analysis by Rand (2016) of research on the role of calculation in agreement to co-operate. From his review of the literature, Rand concludes that co-operative responses based on intuition, shaped by experience, raise joint welfare more than responses based on calculation of short-term benefit to the individual making the assessment.

The 'deficient global response' to enormous numbers of refugees 'in a climate of hostility and xenophobia towards refugees and migrants in many countries' (Anon, 2016) could be a further illustration of this distinction. The problems of enormous numbers of refugees cannot be solved by any rapid, warm-hearted response by individuals and require careful, large-scale planning and massive resources. Do we know the limits of compassion? Does the refugee response in 2016 mark a boundary? How can we help 'the other' on a scale that has certainly not had time to be evolved into our instinctual responses, whatever these may be? See Maley (2016) for consideration of some of these questions.

Variations in response to situations where altruism may be manifested may also result from individual differences. Studies of twins suggest that altruism, as defined for survey purposes, has a range large enough to ensure different responses to given circumstance and heritability of more than 0.5 (Rushton *et al.* 1986). It is to be expected that environment may have a substantial effect on complex, socially dependent traits, as Haldane (1932, p. 25) noted earlier: 'it probably depends to a considerable extent on environment whether the quick-tempered child will develop into a fury or a kindly but impulsive person, the calmer personality into a heartless or benevolent.'

3.3 Competition

Competition occurs. For example, when it rains in late summer, the seeds of many plants germinate, and plant species have many different 'strategies' to ensure that some seedlings survive. The invasive weed *Echium plantagineum*, widespread in Australia, begins to produce a rosette, a ring of leaves that spreads rapidly, as soon as the seed leaves have reached the light. The rapid availability of this fleshy rosette, which is highly palatable to sheep, is part of

the reason why the species is called Salvation Jane in parts of Australia as well as Peterson's Curse, from its weedy nature. Salvation Jane's main 'strategy' is to spread via seeds; a stand of the plant can produce 30,000 seeds per square metre, and these are readily carried by animals and water. The plant competes successfully with many other 'open country' species and can help or hinder human activity. It is seen as 'good' according as whether one is a bee-keeper or a drought-afflicted pastoralist on the one hand or any other rural landholder on the other.

Competition is common, but as we now recognise in the excesses of 19th century 'Social Darwinism', this does not mean that it is in any way virtuous or otherwise. Indeed, Engels, among others, noted that identification of competition in the natural world could be seen to be a transposition of ideas of capitalism into that natural world, and that one can "transfer these theories back again from the natural world to the history of society" (Engels, 1880, p. 584, cited by Rozzi, 1999 p. 919) but there is no necessary transfer of ethics either way. The behaviour of an obligate carnivore, for example, has no necessary implications for that of a human.

Nevertheless, the fact that most human societies appear to have been, and to be today, unequal in the availability of resources to individuals, is important for the future of humanity. Almost any consideration of society addresses inequality in some way; increased competition, unregulated, has always led to increased disamenity for the many at the expense of the favoured few. On utilitarian grounds, this is harmful, and on many revelation-based ethical systems, it is bad. It is not an inference from the states of nature.

As de Duve (2009a, p. 160) wrote, 'human history is a continuous succession of wars and conflicts'; competition taken to a point of violence is normal, even though war is regarded as abnormal. Any ethics, whether drawn from nature or revelation, must incorporate how to reduce this incessant violence, but non-violent state of nature involving sentient beings have proven hard to imagine, let alone bring about.

3.4 Extinction

Extinction is the norm, so death appears certain, not just for an individual but for a species. Ethical judgement of the disaster of human-induced extinction of other species (as in use of the word 'disaster') is a judgement of something that is normal, and hence the ethics must come from outside biology.

In the same way, how individual extinction, or death, occurs in humans is a matter for human ethics, not an inference from knowledge of other animals. As Darwin wrote in a letter to a French correspondent in early 1880 (Darwin 1903–5, pp. 444–5):

> I suppose that no one can prove that death is inevitable, but the evidence in favour of this belief is overwhelmingly strong from the evidence of all other living creatures. I do not believe that it is by any means invariably true that the higher organisms always live longer than its lower ones. Elephants, parrots, ravens, tortoises and some fish all live longer than man. As evolution depends on a long succession of generations, which implies death, it seems to me in the highest degree improbable that man should cease to follow the general law of evolution, and this would follow if he were to be immortal.

Death is normal; more people are dead than alive. What ethical inferences can we draw from the necessity of death? What prolongation of life is appropriate? Should we draw on 'The New Decalogue': 'Thou shalt not kill but needst not strive/Officiously to keep alive'? What can we say about suicide?

3.5 Suicide

Suicide appears to occur in all human societies, though it is almost always more common in males than females. Brunetière (below, par. 16) claimed 'in the whole of Europe, over the last fifty or sixty years [1830–1890], the number of suicides has more than tripled[.] In the Congo, there is hardly a suicide'. The evidence for his statement is hard to find; certainly today both parts of Congo have lower suicide rates than many European countries, including France and Belgium (World Health Organisation 2015). It is not clear that its incidence is a clear indicator or the ethical or economic health of a society, as Brunetière has implied.

Suicide's incidence can change substantially over time; Brunetière was correct about this. For example, it has almost doubled in men worldwide between 1950 and today, whereas it has hardly changed in women over this period (Bertolote and Fleischmann 2002). In a particular society, it can change significantly over short periods of time. For example, in Australia between 2000 and 2009 it fell from 20/100,000 to 15/100,000 in males and from 5.2/100,000 to 4.4 in females (Australian Bureau of Statistics 2012). Furthermore, the rate can be influenced by identifiable aspects of the environment: drought increases the risk of suicide in middle-aged men but not women in rural Australian (Nicholls *et al.*, 2006; Hanigan *et al.* 2012). There is a genetical component to the causation of suicidal behaviour (Voracek and Loibl 2007), with a broad-sense heritability of about 0.2 (Roy *et al.* 1991), but environmental influences are very strong: believers in an afterlife are much less likely to wish to reach it early than unbelievers (Bertolote and Fleischmann 2002).

As many have argued, how we value the external world is an ethical choice. Many would choose a world with high biodiversity and a low rate of extinction, if possible, valuing other species for their very difference, not simply for their attractiveness. We may learn that the level of stability in an ecosystem depends functionally on the level of biodiversity (McCann, 2000) and that it can be important in ecosystem revival (e.g. Kaiser-Bunbury *et al.* 2017). If stability is important for survival of the ecosystem in the face of external shocks (e.g. anthropogenic global warming), then we may come to value diversity more highly. If such global warming is occurring, then is a decision to attempt to prevent it because of certain loss of biodiversity an ethical decision or simply an expedient decision based on self-interest?

If we consider diversity in the light just described, as making survival of an ecosystem less unlikely, and the same applying to the population of any species can we then say that diversity is desirable for the species to have a future? Would this make respect for human diversity an imperative? I think that Subramaniam (2014) would say yes (e.g. 'the politics of assimilation' pp. 152–3). It is, however, not enough to say, with Julian Huxley, 'I believe in diversity' (J. Huxley, 1941, p. 299), and therefore to answer yes to my two questions.

A specimen of the short-nosed echidna (*Tachyglossus aculeata*) approaching the author's feet. This monotrem (egg-laying mammal) is in danger of extinction through human activity. Taxonomically further from the common hedgehog (*Erinaceus europaeus*) than is the house mouse (*Mus musclulus*) from humans, the echidna has evolved similar external defence to the hedgehog (section 3.10).

3.6 Reciprocal mutualism

This is defined as behaviour which both reduces an organism's fitness and increases a different organism's fitness, on the expectation that the second organism will reciprocate; it is therefore not altruism by definition, and while it is related to co-operation, it is not the same thing. The maxim 'do as you would be done by' is an easier way to state the principle behind the definition.

Mutualism can be invaded by 'cheating'. Salazar *et al.* (2015) have found two quite different interactions between an aphid *Paracletus cimiciformis* and ants of the genus *Tetramorium*. In one case, the ants obtain honeydew from the aphids, cleaning the aphids in return the ants may also aid in deterring predation of the aphids. (This reciprocal relationship is widespread among ants and aphids.) In the other case, Salazara *et al.* have found that individuals of a genetically identical and clonally produced morph (termed 'flat') of the same species are carried into the ants' nest, where they are treated by the ants as if they were larvae of the ants' own species. Here, the aphids pierce actual ant larvae and drink their haemolymph. Salazara *et al.* have found chemical 'similarities between *T. semilaeve* ant larvae and flat aphids greater than between the two genetically identical aphid morphs', suggesting that the flat aphids are mimicking the ants' recognition signals. They conclude that they have discovered a case of 'aggressive mimicry' in which the benefits are sharply skewed towards the aphids.

Aggressive mimicry, which involves 'cheating', is clearly a trans-specific behaviour which is not a model for 'good behaviour'. How it evolved is not clear. The authors write (p. 1105) 'The fact that flat morph aphids inside ant nests give rise, when harsh conditions are over, to four morphs representing life history strategies adapted to different temporal and spatial uncertainties ... suggests that the flat morph is at the centre of a diversified strategy for survival and recolonization of the aphid host plants.' This raises additional questions. (For example, is the 'strategy' that of the individual or the group? I have not considered group selection because it answers too

many questions through its necessary assumptions; group morality is inbuilt.)

Although cheating might be expected to destabilise the mutualism which it parasitises, as in a bacterium *Myxobacterium xanthus* (Fiegna and Velicer, 2003), this need not be the case. Ferriere *et al.* (2002) discuss evidence that beneficial mutualism and cheating can coexist for lengthy evolutionary periods, and conclude that under such circumstances, mutualism should improve. Because comparisons are of phenomena in very different taxa, the components of cheating discussed below in 3.7 should be unravelled. One can conclude that it is widespread and has occurred over very long evolutionary times; it is not always lost to natural selection.

3.6.1 Co-operation

Co-operation means working together, a joint activity involving therefore at least two individuals, probably towards some common purpose. The purpose does not have to be chosen by those engaged in co-operation and indeed may not be evident in the activity.

How co-operation evolved is not clear. It is evident in the behaviour of all social animals, so must have evolved independently in many lineages, even if the same biochemistry is used. Wei *et al.* (2015) wrote: 'Another essential facet of social behaviour, the adaptive reinforcement of interactions among members of a group (i.e., the reward of being social), requires the oxytocin-dependent induction of long-term synaptic plasticity at excitatory synapses of the nucleus accumbens (NAc) (12), a key region in the brain reward circuit.' This kind of apparently basic physiological-biochemical mechanism can only function when all components are present, yet it is essential for higher-order functions like social behaviour; I say nothing here about brain function in general, given the immensity of the subject and the smallness of the chosen example (not to mention my lack of specialist knowledge).

Modelling of such social behaviour is very crude compared with the complex physiology that actually underlies the behaviour. Hormonal responses can arise from so many different environmental stimuli. For example, cortisol can be modulated by one's gut microbiota (Schmidt *et al.*, 2015) or by the sound of a baby crying, a sound which will also elicit a cortisol response in dogs (Yong and Ruffman, 2014).

This is not to say that simple models cannot be useful, as has already been emphasized. Trust, a level of which is necessary for effective co-operation, can be shown in simple models to be sustained in various ways. For example, Jordan *et al.* (2016, pp. 476, 473) have proposed the following:

> ...we help answer a fundamental question regarding human nature: why do humans care about selfish behaviours that do not affect them personally?

> Third-party-punishment (TPP)..., in which unaffected observers punish selfishness, promotes cooperation by deterring defection. ... TPP is a costly signal of trustworthiness [and individuals differ in their propensities towards these costs and benefits]. ... individuals for whom trustworthiness [is important will tend towards the acceptance of TPP and hence] ... it can be advantageous for individuals to punish selfishness in order to signal that they are not selfish themselves.

They have shown that such behaviours can occur in role-play and have modelled their system to show that it can be stable, in a game-theoretic sense.

From a crude model like this an evolutionary model can be built that permits the evolution of the costly but not altruistic behaviour of TPP.

Edwards (2009) has argued for the importance of tolerance in the evolution of interspecific co-operation. He has drawn a number of conclusions that bear on how co-operation might be regarded outside an ethical framework: 'tolerance [may decrease] the cost/benefit ratio of interacting with an antagonist'; partner choice and partner-fidelity feedback similarly decrease the cost/

benefit ratio of interaction; and 'cheating' will reduce interaction in a partnership.

3.7 Cheating

Cheating has been introduced in the previous section. In normal parlance, as accepted above, cheating implies consciousness and purpose, but according to Ghoul *et al.* (2014), it needs to be defined carefully to be useful as an evolutionary concept. They classify cheating on four criteria: the possibility of co-operation; whether deception is used; whether the behaviour is intraspecific or interspecific; and whether the 'cheater' can choose between behaviours.

An example may make this clearer. Here is Charles Darwin on the behaviour of cuckoos, from the first edition of the *Origin of Species*:

> 'It is now commonly admitted that the more immediate and final cause of the cuckoo's instinct is, that she lays her eggs, not daily, but at intervals of two or three days; so that, if she were to make her own nest and sit on her own eggs, those first laid would have to be left for some time unincubated, or there would be eggs and young birds of different ages in the same nest. If this were the case, the process of laying and hatching might be inconveniently long, more especially as she has to migrate at a very early period; and the first hatched young would probably have to be fed by the male alone. But the American cuckoo is in this predicament; for she makes her own nest and has eggs and young successively hatched, all at the same time. It has been asserted that the American cuckoo occasionally lays her eggs in other birds' nests; but I hear on the high authority of Dr. Brewer, that this is a mistake. Nevertheless, I could give several instances of various birds which have been known occasionally to lay their eggs in other birds' nests. Now let us suppose that the ancient progenitor of our European cuckoo had the habits

of the American cuckoo; but that occasionally she laid an egg in another bird's nest. If the old bird profited by this occasional habit, or if the young were made more vigorous by advantage having been taken of the mistaken maternal instinct of another bird, than by their own mother's care, encumbered as she can hardly fail to be by having eggs and young of different ages at the same time; then the old birds or the fostered young would gain an advantage. And analogy would lead me to believe, that the young thus reared would be apt to follow by inheritance the occasional and aberrant habit of their mother, and in their turn would be apt to lay their eggs in other birds' nests, and thus be successful in rearing their young. By a continued process of this nature, I believe that the strange instinct of our cuckoo could be, and has been, generated. I may add that, according to Dr. Gray and to some other observers, the European cuckoo has not utterly lost all maternal love and care for her own offspring.

The occasional habit of birds laying their eggs in other birds' nests, either of the same or of a distinct species, is not very uncommon with the Gallinaceae; and this perhaps explains the origin of a singular instinct in the allied group of ostriches. For several hen ostriches, at least in the case of the American species, unite and lay first a few eggs in one nest and then in another; and these are hatched by the males. This instinct may probably be accounted for by the fact of the hens laying a large number of eggs; but, as in the case of the cuckoo, at intervals of two or three days. This instinct, however, of the American ostrich has not as yet been perfected; for a surprising number of eggs lie strewed over the plains, so that in one day's hunting I picked up no less than twenty lost and wasted eggs.

By the sixth edition, Darwin was able to write that virtually everything he had reported had been confirmed in other species, especially Australian cuckoos. His speculations on mechanism have required more than a hundred and fifty years to be supported, modified or corrected. It is noteworthy that many birds, e.g. some thrushes (Samas *et al.* 2014), have evolved sensitive egg recognition so that they remove cuckoos' eggs from their nests. In the magpie *Pica* the same phenomenon is observed, though the parents defend the nest more strongly against predators than against the nest parasitiser (the great spotted cuckoo *Clamator glandarius*) (Soler *et al.* 1999). In both cases, a protective mechanism that is 'good for the species' has been evolved, but as usual by benefits to individual lineages.

Much is still to be learnt about brood parasitism, since empirical results do not always bear out theory. For example, Fossøy *et al.* (2012) found that maternally determined sex ratio in parasitic cuckoo offspring did not vary as expected with the quality of host species as rearers (more males where rearer quality was higher). These findings need conformation and explanation, and a better understanding of brood parasitism should result, but the general conclusion persists that cheating can be of great evolutionary advantage, despite its anthropocentric opprobrium.

Another well-known case of 'cheating' is provided by polyandry and polygyny in passerine birds considered to be socially monogamous. There has been a lengthy debate about the costs and benefits of extra-pair mating (EPM). For males, the advantages are clear, and similar to those for cuckoos: paternal expenditure on gene survival is reduced. For females, the advantages are less clear. It has been suggested that female birds with a partner may benefit under good environmental conditions from EPM in contributing more genes to subsequent generations on account of the diversity of the male contribution. In a review, Arnqvist and Kirkpatrick (2005) suggested that this was unlikely because selection against the success of EPY (extra-pair young) is strong. They presented estimates of this selection as d_{EW}, the difference between fitness of

EPY and WPY (within-pair young): most values were very small, with a mean not different from zero. Their conclusion was that indirect selection could produce tiny changes at best, hence acting very slowly. They then considered direct selection on EPM behaviour in females brought about by reduced paternal care and found that it would was significantly different from zero such as to reduce EPM substantially over time. They concluded that direct negative effects of reduced paternal care would militate against females engaging in EPM to such an extent that the indirect selection on EPM would be overwhelmed. (Hasselquist and Sherman (2001) had earlier presented evidence that polygyny and EPM were negatively associated, partly because of the direct negative effects concluded by Arnqvist and Kirkpatrick to be important.)

It is tempting to compare the case of these birds with outbreeding plant species that can partly self-pollinate or which can self-pollinate at season's end or under other less favourable environmental circumstances. For example, many forest Eucalypts exhibit about 70% outcrossing. Most theoretical work on the spread of genes permitting selfing suggests that self-pollination will become universal within a species, yet this is not the case. Even in the case where a single mutant gene allows selfing, as in the case of the homostyle primula, fixation does not occur (Curtis and Curtis 1985). Few would say that the plants

achieving offspring through such breakdown of outbreeding mechanisms had cheated or committed incest.

Plants can give out chemical signals from their roots that mimic bacterial signals and thereby confuse the frequency-dependent signalling that permits a population of bacteria to co-ordinate the regulation of gene expression. This allows the plants to avoid damage or to mitigate it (Bauer and Mathesius, 2004).

Charles Robert Darwin (1809–1882) was foremost in effecting a revolution in European understanding of humans' place in nature. Brunetière's called Darwin's writings 'novels', but evolution by natural selection is as well supported by evidence as any scientific theory. (Frontispiece of volume 1 of Francis Darwin 1887: Life and Letters of Charles Darwin. London, John Murray).

3.7.1 Mimicry

Mimicry is perhaps the clearest example of 'original sin' in species other than *Homo sapiens*. An organism trades on the strengths or weaknesses of another species or simply harnesses the energy of that other species to 'further its own ends'. It also furnishes clear examples of interspecific co-operation.

Plant mimicry is not unusual, and one of the earliest speculations on the subject seems to have been that of Robert Brown, who thought that the flowers of the almost entirely self-pollinated bee orchid *Ophrys apifera* 'resembled bees in order to deter their visits, but this seems extremely improbable. The flowers with their pink sepals do not resemble any British bee, and it is probably true … that the plant received its name merely from the hairy labellum being somewhat like the abdomen of a humble-bee.' (Darwin, 1862/1904, p. 56) Darwin further claimed that insects almost never visited the bee orchid, though such rare visitors would move pollen and effect rare cross-pollination.

The origin of the bee orchid's curious form of mimicry remains uncertain, but most plant mimicry seems to involve some reciprocity, equal or unequal. Schiestl (2005) reviewed mimicry in orchids from this point of view, since about one third of all pollinator attraction mechanisms, whether through mimicry or otherwise, appear to offer nothing to the pollinator in exchange from the time and energy used in the insect's visit to the plant. He concluded that the high rates of speciation in orchids are related to the plant-insect interactions that drive outbreeding, and that floral morphology has been important in these processes.

The general conclusion seems to be that cheating through mimicry is widespread and that it persists in orchids because outbreeding is facilitated. It could be speculated that the propensity to co-operate underlies all of these unequal exchanges, and that co-operation is somehow a more fundamental mechanism than those that are built on it. The finding that spontaneous co-operation appears to depend on personal social orientation (towards the group or towards the self) (Mischkowski and Glöckner, 2016) is not in accord with this speculation.

3.8 Size

Size is important. The human brain is out of allometric proportion when compared with other primates. As Lankester (1907, pp. 24–5) wrote: 'Man, it would seem, at a very remote period attained the extraordinary development of brain which marked him off from the rest of the animal world, but has ever since been developing the powers and qualities of this organ without increasing its size, or materially altering in other bodily features.'

As we slowly fill in gaps in the fossil record, our knowledge of the rapid increase in brain size has grown, but we know nothing of the extinction of the other human-like primates which took part in these changes. We do not know if brain evolution is an example of Fisher's (1999, p. 137; 1930/1999, pp. 305–8) 'runaway process', in which sexual selection was important, nor whether there is an optimal brain size. (Many traits, such as openness to argument, probably require a minimum brain size, but it is not clear how this might be determined.)

The concept of 'being the right size' was introduced by Haldane (1928, in the essay entitled 'on being the right size'):

> The most obvious differences between different animals are differences of size, but for some reason the zoologists have paid singularly little attention to them. In a large textbook of zoology before me I find no indication that the eagle is larger than the sparrow, or the hippopotamus bigger than the hare, though some grudging admissions are made in the case of the mouse and the whale. But yet it is easy to show that a hare could not be as large as a hippopotamus, or a whale as small as a herring. For every type of animal there is a most convenient size, and a large change in size inevitably carries with it a change of form.

Haldane went on to point out that increased size, with physical, chemical and biological constraints, was generally advantageous: 'rightness' could include the evolution of larger size. Smith J.M. (1968) provides access to the physical calculations which underlie Haldane's argument. See also Mayo (1983).

This use of 'right' means 'efficient and effective in the context of the ecological niche occupied by the particular animal species'. It does not mean 'right and proper' in the ethical sense. However, Haldane went on from individuals to consider societies:

> And just as there is a best size for every animal, so the same is true for every human institution. In the Greek type of

democracy all the citizens could listen to a series of orators and vote directly on questions of legislation. Hence their philosophers held that a small city was the largest possible democratic state. The English invention of representative government made a democratic nation possible, and the possibility was first realized in the United States, and later elsewhere. With the development of broadcasting it has once more become possible for every citizen to listen to the political views of representative orators, and the future may perhaps see the return of the national state to the Greek form of democracy. Even the referendum has been made possible only by the institution of daily newspapers.

To the biologist the problem of socialism appears largely as a problem of size. The extreme socialists desire to run every nation as a single business concern. I do not suppose that Henry Ford would find much difficulty in running Andorra or Luxembourg on a socialistic basis. He has already more men on his pay-roll than their population. It is conceivable that a syndicate of Fords, if we could find them, would make Belgium Ltd or Denmark Inc. pay their way. But while nationalization of certain industries is an obvious possibility in the largest of states, I find it no easier to picture a completely socialized British Empire or United States than an elephant turning somersaults or a hippopotamus jumping a hedge.

There is evidence for the efficiency and effectiveness of different-sized groups. This applies to kelp-bed filter feeders (Stuart and Klumpp 1984) and to humans working on intellectual tasks in groups (Dennis and Valacich 1994). For adult humans working together on tasks, groups of 7–15 have been shown to be efficient for some tasks, whereas working as individuals or in very small groups may be better for others.

Franklin's number gives the minimum size of a population in which inbreeding depression and chance will not give an unacceptably high chance of extinction (Franklin, 1980). It has been shown that loss of genetical variability generally increases the probability of a population's extinction (Newman and Pilson 1997), but the population sizes concerned are so low that they are not relevant to humans as a current species. They are, however, relevant to the current extinctions that are driven by the weight of humanity, and humanity's expansion across the face of the earth (Avery, 2014).

Species biomass gives an indication of a species's 'place in nature', in the sense that body size is negatively associated with species number. Ants, perhaps the most numerous animals on earth, are estimated to number more than a million milliard and to have biomass across all ant taxa of 30–300 million tonnes (Mt). Elephants have biomass of 0.1 Mt. Orangutans with average mass around 50 kg have biomass 5 Mt or less. Cattle have biomass over 500 Mt; there are over one milliard cattle. Humans number almost 7 milliard and have biomass over 300 Mt.

Human biomass is not in line with than of other mammalian species; it is far greater than would be expected for human average body mass. Lankester (1907, pp. 40–1) wrote 'By rebelling against Nature's method, Man has made himself the only animal which constantly increases in number. Whenever disease is controlled his increase will be still more rapid than at present.' This prediction has been amply fulfilled. Lankester was not being a Malthusian when he wrote the prediction, merely stating what technological advances would bring about.

Social insects provide no guide to optimal species size. First, a social insect colony is not a good analogy to a human settlement because of biological specialisation and other basic differences (Freeman 1921). Secondly, social insects offer enormous differences in models. For example, Gadagkar (2001) found that colony fission i.e. division to give two new colonies could occur successfully in *Ropalidia marginata* with an initial colony size barely in double figures, despite this species having multiple castes.

Whatever may be the advantage to social animals, and ants and humans seem to demonstrate that there may be one, it is not clear that maximising species number is part of that advantage. Maximising utility ('well-being') by maximising it for the current population may not be sustainable past the short term.

3.9 Dollo's Law

This law or rule or generalisation simply states that the course of evolution cannot reverse itself. In particular, if a function is lost, it will not re-emerge in the same lineage. (In the case of sexual dimorphism in loss of function, as for flight in certain cockroach lineages, for example, Dollo's law would not apply, since the 'flight genes' are still present and functional, simply suppressed in one sex.) This latter statement is a statistical one; there is a very low probability of mutations to restore function to genes whose function has been lost. It could be taken to be an example of *Luke* 9:62 ('No man, having put his hand to the plough, and looking back, is fit for the kingdom of God') in practice, but more a prime illustration of the contingent nature of evolution by natural selection, the selection always being among the variants available. Because it is a generalisation from observation, and has potential or actual exceptions, it is probably part of the reason why Fain (*loc. cit.*) claims that there are no evolutionary laws. For Brunetière, on the other hand, regression, of which loss of function is an example, was very important, but always related to the Fall of Man (Brunetière par. 23 below).

Two independent studies have partly elucidated the loss of legs in the evolution of snakes (Kvon *et al.* 2016, Leal and Cohn 2016). The latter study also provides evidence of a possible pathway for the re-evolution of legs after they were lost, a counter-example to Dollo's Law.

Does the evolution of a function mean it is still available, even it is suppressed, as in the case just mentioned? For example, if co-operation evolves in a lineage, the genes involved will not be silenced or otherwise lost unless their function ceases to be necessary, and epistatic interactions can mean that other functions keep the particular genes active. Change of social structure might change what was needed, but social interaction would still occur, such a change being unlike the loss of sight in cave-living animals.

What is the genetic architecture of co-operation? Is it susceptible to changes that might lead to its loss? In a social insect, the fire ant *Solenopsis invicta*, several different behaviour patterns, in queens and workers, are influenced by one particular gene (or small region marked by this gene). Keller (2009, p. 3211) wrote:

> This example illustrates the danger of searching for adaptive explanations without a clear understanding of the genetic basis of the behaviour. The consideration of selection at the individual or colony levels only would have led to an erroneous explanation of why workers eliminate the heavier and more fecund queens in polygyne colonies. This is an important point, in particular because of the current confusion by many scientists in how selection works at the different levels of biological organization.

> Similarly, it is likely that the interpretation of the social behaviours of many other organisms would change if one had information on their genetic bases. In this respect, it should be mentioned that pleiotropy is probably the rule rather than the exception for many traits, particularly for behaviours which are the product of many sensory, integrative, motivational and motor processes.

Single genes influencing a trait are most readily acted upon by natural selection, when the environment changes suddenly, as is seen in insecticide resistance in pest organisms; the pattern of response to selection is unlike that obtained in the laboratory, as noted elsewhere (section 2.3). Hence, a gene like that just discussed could produce at-risk phenotypes.

The 'ethical imperative' expressed in the maxim 'use it or lose it' could be said to derive from Dollo's Law, but its normative force, if any, does not inhere in its ancestry. Thoday (1958) attempted to induce a general idea of progress that would include regression: 'biological progress [is] an increase in fitness for survival'. Such 'progress' then can include loss of function that benefits individuals living in an environment where that function is neutral or harmful. However, it is not progress in the sense that, say, a Nissan Leaf represents progress (in cost, safety, reliability, comfort and performance) from the electric car 'Jamais Contente' in which Camille Jenatzy set a land speed record of over 100 kph in 1899. It is certainly not progress in Brunetière's sense.

3.10 Multiple pathways to the same constrained objective

Does the course of evolution exhibit phenomena in which 'the end justifies the means'? Of course 'justification' is not an evolutionary concept; it is an ethical one, but what is the evidence? That is to say, what is the evidence for selection of different sub-traits in the evolution of a function? In a sense, this is how natural selection might have broken Dollo's Law, should an example of such a breach be recognised: an 'objective', that is to say a function constrained by physics and chemistry might be re-evolved by different pathways from the original.

Evolution of flight is one of the clearest examples: flight has evolved independently at least four times: in pterosaurs, in birds, in bats and in insects. The historical or contingent nature of evolution by natural selection is very evident here; there may be a 'best' anatomy for flight on the basis of the vertebrate quadruped *Bauplan*,

in which case at least one lineage must be non-optimal and based on an inferior model. Whatever the *Bauplan*, the path to improvement will be clear, since, for example, small improvements in wing area will almost always lead to improved flight performance, given the physical constraints on flight (Mayo 1983).

Competing demands from selection influencing different traits produce many other changes in wings that are not optimal for flight. For example, reduction in wing size below what would be optimal for flight is not unusual in insect lineages (e.g. Roff 1994). Kotyk and Varadínová 2017) investigated experimental wing reduction in a cockroach *Eublaberus distanti* and found that it reduced mating success in males but not overall fitness in females. They concluded that the existence of species with flying males and wingless females could be explained by divergent selection in the two sexes. Optimization, if it was occurring, was directionally different in the two sexes.

Possibly more curious is the case of convergence in mimicry reported by Maruyama and Parker (2017), whereby beetles from different taxa have evolved mimicry to particular army ants in lineages separated by large phylogenetic distances, 'as much as 105 million years' (p. 1). The particular genes involved are not known, but instead of simply meeting the physical, physiological and behavioural requirements for individual flight, the beetles have had to achieve phenotypic, scent and behavioural similarity sufficient to deceive nest guardians. Optimality in every case seems unlikely. Maruyama and Parker (p. 5) claim that the repeated similar mimicry or symbiosis that they appear to have discovered challenges Gould's (1990, and at immensely greater length in 2002) hypothesis that evolution is highly contingent; that from any given point, the future course of evolution cannot be predicted. The hypothesis could be rescued by considering the particular genes involved in every case: the prediction would be that they will not always be the same. Nevertheless, the outcome illustrates the power of natural selection in achieving an apparent end, where there is in fact no purpose as such.

3.11 Positive attributes and flaws

Much of my focus has been on the research-based evidence on problematic rather than positive traits; this has been because the ethical questions of interest tend to involve such traits; few seek to solve problems that they do not perceive to exist. Darwin, of course, having convinced himself that we are the outcome of evolution by natural selection, tried to explain everything that came to his capacious mind or was drawn to his attention. Did the idea and perception of beauty arise from sexual selection, females associating what they desired with what was, on some scale other than mating, better than what they did not desire? Did laughter arise from relief at the passing of danger? He was constantly asking these questions, probably aware that they did not, in themselves, have an ethical dimension.

Traits with negative attributes can be measured, and sometimes there is a dimension from 'good' to 'bad', as in 'happy' to 'sad', but not always. The heritability of loneliness is 0.4–0.6 (McGuire and Clifford 2000; Boomsma *et al.* 2005); the heritabilities of stoicism, indifference to one's perceived state of loneliness or dislike of close company, all traits that may be opposed to loneliness, do not appear to be clearly known. These traits may also influence grieving, so that for any given individual the outcome of extreme loss will not be predictable. The psychological traits with the greatest robustness as subjects of investigation are not necessarily those of the greatest interest for evolutionary or ethical enquiry.

Darwin (1872, pp. 80) noted that grief 'and some other states of mind appear to be at first exciting, but soon become depressing to an extreme degree'. He noted further that grief and some of its external manifestations were found in all human groups and in some other animals, but that expression varied. Grief is associated with longing and awareness of separation, both traits that could have survival value, in terms of behaviour when lost or otherwise separated from the group. Depression, on the other hand, is difficult to view as the outcome of some selectively advantageous process. Its heritability lies between 0.3 and 0.5, and is higher in females than in males (Kendler *et al.*, 2006). It is present in most cultures; what is its origin? At this point, one is engaged in pure speculation. For example, Segal *et al.* (1995) wrote '[t]he finding [in a large twin study] of a negative association between age at loss [of a co-twin] and magnitude of bereavement-related behaviors in anticipated by evolutionary reasoning. This relationship is consistent with the expectation of a loss in reproductive fitness of the deceased with advancing age, and a consequent reduction in grief-related behaviors.'

Overall, evolution by natural selection provides no direct guide to 'improvements' in human behaviour.

3.12 'Seven deadly sins'

Recognition of a biological role in the causation of 'sins' does not imply biological determinism in any way. Indeed, it has been advocated that treatment of 'sinners' and 'criminals' should be built on recognition of its biological component. The disappointing work of Thornhill and Palmer (2000) has already been discussed in this regard. The more cautious approach of Mednick and Finello (1983) should not be neglected.

Determinism and free will are discussed later. Here, it should be noted particularly that genetical determinism is not possible. The possibility of genetical, environmental and interactive effects was built into the first method for analysis of the sources of variation in quantitative biological variation (Fisher, 1918), and such methods have been central to studies of quantitative variation ever since, with recognition of their limitations (Mayo 2011). Partly for ethical reasons associated with such aberrations as *Rassenhygiene*, genetical determinism has been rejected as a possibility, at the same time as its impossibility has been demonstrated. A much-used simple example is that of the human disorder phenylketonuria, in which a recessive genetical defect leads, in the homozygote, to an inability to utilise the amino acid phenylalanine normally. Unrecognised, such individuals develop abnormally, with profound intellectual impairment. Identified soon after birth with a simple test used almost universally in rich countries, these homozygotes are given a special diet and develop normally. A change in the environment prevents what would otherwise be a certain developmental outcome.

Despite the knowledge that genetical determinism is impossible, some find the idea present in people's minds and seek to eliminate its consideration. For example, Noble (2006) wrote a whole book to dispel the idea, without being able to quote a single genetical determinist's views of the kinds that need to be rejected. Noble was concerned to counter the idea popularised by Dawkins (1976) that genes are the central focus of natural selection, when of course from Darwin onwards the organism has been recognised as the object of natural selection. (Dawkins, of course, understood this, but his powerful writing conveyed a different impression to some.)

Darwin, without knowing the physical basis of heredity, was concerned to identify and demonstrate the continuity in behaviour across humans and other animals. In his *Expression of the emotions*, Darwin (1872, p. 262) wrote 'Jealousy, envy, avarice, revenge, suspicion, deceit, slyness, guilt, vanity, conceit, ambition, pride, humility, etc. – It is doubtful whether the greater number of the above complex states of mind are revealed by any fixed expression, sufficiently distinct to be described or delineated.' He excepted conceit, and pointed to how its attributes hauteur and puffed-up-ness could be seen in other species in response to threat or to impose a threat. What was clear was that different species had the same behaviours manifesting the same biological needs; sin had no role in the play. The film villain elaborately and absurdly planning to emasculate the hero with a laser is no different in principle from another ape seeing off a rival with teeth and hands.

Sins can be seen to be the tails of distributions of propensities or tendencies to certain behaviours, an old idea (e.g. Guyau 1885, chapter 4).

3.12.1 Avarice

'Miserliness is heritable' is the title of a paper by Hur *et al.* (2011), but heritability = 0.28 in their Korean sample, which is not very high, though significantly greater than zero. Miserliness is only part of avarice, the part relating to the retention of what is desired and obtained.

Avarice also includes the desire and its focus, in general, on possessions, not simply on wealth as in the primary definition. Perception of normal needs at the bottom of Maslow's hierarchy will vary, so that extreme longing or yearning is simply the tail of the distribution, whatever its shape, of desire.

3.12.2 Pride

As noted above, Darwin considered that conceit, which is closely related to pride, could be physically recognised, and that its outward manifestation could be related to widespread defensive and offensive behaviour in other animals. From this point of view, these behaviours had evolved under natural selection; they could also have evolved particularly by sexual selection, though that is simple speculation.

The genetics of pride does not appear to have been extensively studied. Self-esteem is not the same thing, but it has been well considered, and is heritable ($h^2 = 0.4$ or greater; Roy *et al.* 1995). It is still open to change by natural selection.

3.12.3 Lust

Virtually every approach to human behaviour, whether theological, scientific or otherwise, recognises that the urge to procreate is instinctual, built-in. This urge is necessary for non-parthenogenetic reproduction in animals and has its equivalent in the reproduction of animals. 'Lust' is a label applied either to the tail of the distribution of sexual activity or to particular sexual behaviour unacceptable in some philosophy.

3.12.3.1 Sexuality

Sexuality is perhaps where we see the naturalistic fallacy most inextricably intertwined into our thinking. Heterosexual behaviour leading to coition is the norm in animal species with two sexes. Rare exceptions, such as parthenogenesis in a number of species, do not disturb the generality of this statement. Many have, over the centuries, noted that this is the biological norm, something essential in most animal species for the survival of the species. It has, however, frequently been codified as what is right in some moral or ethical sense, and hence what is to be enforced by law. Sanctioned structures for the heterosexual relationship (monogamy, serial monogamy, polygamy, polygyny…) have not always been the same, but in most cases non-heterosexual relationships have not been acceptable. The Anglican Book of Common Prayer gives voice to the concept:

> Dearly beloved, we are gathered together here in the sight of God, and in the face of this congregation, to join together this Man and this Woman in holy Matrimony; which is an honourable estate, instituted of God in the time of man's innocency, signifying unto us the mystical union that is betwixt Christ and his Church; which holy estate Christ adorned and beautified with his presence, and first miracle that he wrought, in Cana of Galilee; and is commended of Saint Paul to be honourable among all men: and therefore is not by any to

be enterprised, nor taken in hand, unadvisedly, lightly, or wantonly, to satisfy men's carnal lusts and appetites, like brute beasts that have no understanding; but reverently, discreetly, advisedly, soberly, and in the fear of God; duly considering the causes for which Matrimony was ordained.

The assertions in these statements rest on revelation. The institution of marriage, in the Christian tradition, is built on the recognition of the fundamental nature of desire, and indeed lust (1 *Corinthians* 7:8–9), without appeal to revelation.

Evidence on sex is extraordinarily varied, just in humans; evidence on polygamy, polygyny etc. is hard to collect in humans, and what happens in other animals (e.g. in birds, Jarvi *et al.*, 1982 and much subsequent work) is hard to associate closely with humans.

The heritability of number of sexual partners has been reported as 0.4 (Cherkas *et al*, 2004) Age at first sexual intercourse in the USA has a reported heritability of over 0.3 (Rodgers *et al*. 1999). Sexual activity may be related to activity in general (Plomin, 1986), and there is a substantial genetical component in level of activity, but very few studies of the 'heritability of lust' have been carried out. The evidence on other putative drivers of activity, such as dopamine or pheromones, is equivocal (e.g. Guo *et al*. 2008; Hare *et al*. 2017). Indeed, Guo *et al*. (op. cit., p. 2) have claimed that a dopamine transportase gene is associated with number of sexual partners, an aspect of 'risky sexual behaviour' (defined to include number of sexual partners, age of initiation of sexual activity, use of protection and sexual hygiene), but that this gene's effect is swamped by other environmental factors, and is also dependent on the actual number of partners.

Sex reversal is the norm in some species. When the mechanisms are fully explicated, we shall understand what has evolved (e.g. Sheng *et al*. 2015), and may see whether it has any relevance to 'gender diversity' in humans. The two sets of phenomena clearly not the same.

There appears to be some level of genetical influence on sexual preference in humans, but environmental influences are also important, and results from the modest numbers of studies are not completely in agreement (e.g. Bem 1996, Bailey *et al.* 2000; Guo *et al.*, 2008).

3.12.4 Wrath

Anger has complex genetics, according to Rebollo and Boomsma (2006). In their large twin study, they found that 23% of the phenotypic variance in males was additive genetic, so that narrow heritability was 0.23, whereas in females it was 0.34. However, 26% of the male variance was attributed to dominance effects, that is to say, to the combined departures from additivity of all the genes influencing the trait. Thus, more than half of the variation observed in males was genetical in origin, compared with only one third in females. The participants in the study were young adults, and the authors stated that 'during adolescence and young adulthood, anger tends to decrease with age, while during the adult years there appears to be a slight increase in anger with ageing.' (p. 220)

The authors do not discuss the reasons for the difference between the sexes in genetical causation of anger, and indeed pursue only the idea that a combination of this kind of study with studies of physiological variables might elucidate the claimed relationship between anger and risk of coronary heart disease. It seems likely that genomic studies will unearth the actual genetical differences that underlie the curious ratios listed above, but how they may contribute to direction of behavioural changes is not clear.

3.12.4.1 Aggression

Aggression is usually defined in terms of readiness to attack, partly in the sense of the old saying that 'attack is the best form of defence', partly in the sense that it is the outcome of feelings of antipathy or anger. In this latter sense,

it is a human trait, since in other species the individual cannot be asked about its feelings. Although the word can be simply used to describe a behaviour, it mostly retains some pejorative connotation from its Johnsonian definition: 'the first act of injury; commencement of a quarrel by an act of iniquity'. Lethal violence among humans is found in the fossil record.

When aggression is a strategy of, say, a territorial animal, it simply describes the behaviour of protecting the territory by hostile displays or acts. As such, it can be seen as a necessary response to encroachment on a territory.

Veroude *et al.* (2016, p. 20) wrote 'Aggression is an evolutionarily conserved behaviour that has been studied in many non-human species.' They gave examples of aggression from birds, mammals and arthropods. Many involve territoriality; it would perhaps be better to think of aggression as an environmentally constrained behaviour. A web-spinning spider which obtains its food supply and that for its young through capture in its web will not be expected to exhibit aggression towards its prey, whereas specialised castes of ants defending nests may well use aggression in that defence. Similarly, birds and rodents defending territory may be aggressive towards intruders. The evolved aggressive behaviour is analogous across these widely diverged taxa, just as flight-required structures (wings) are analogous in birds and mammals. Gómez *et al.* (2016, p. 3) have written 'humans have phylogenetically inherited their propensity for violence', on the basis of a thorough analysis of intra-specific violence in mammals; the behaviour could have been conserved across mammalian lineages; genetical analysis is needed.

Studies in other species reveal that aggression is modulated by genes related to the dopamine pathways in widely unrelated species (e.g. *Drosophila*, Alekseyenko *et al.* 2013; poultry, Li *et al.* 2016). Since the dopamine pathway is important very widely, from arthropods to mammals, this might be seen to contradict the argument just set out, but whatever the case, aggression is a widely distributed behaviour, not something anomalous that is confined to a few taxa. Its complexity is being dissected (e.g. Buades-Rotger *et al.* 2016) but these studies do not necessarily bear directly on behaviour in an ethical context.

Lorenz (1965a, p. 83) wrote 'Every animal, above all every larger mammal, *flees* from a superior adversary, as soon as the latter reaches a certain distance from the animal.' The greater the fear, the greater the distance at which flight starts. When surprised or cornered, the animal that would have fled may attack its superior out of desperation. Such an attack would be quite distinct from aggression; it is very necessary to ascertain the circumstances in considering aggression.

In a different context, Lorenz (1965b, p. 20) wrote '...the belief that human aggression is based not on phylogenetic adaptation but on learning implies a tremendous underassessment of its dangers. Hitherto this belief has only led to the production of thousands of intolerably aggressive non-frustrated children, but it may lead to much worse things.' Here, a strong ethical judgement is drawn from evolutionary considerations, but the normative aspect of the judgement is not dependent on the evolutionary events as such. The key point in the balance of nature and nurture, which was not settled at the time. This is not to say that it is settled now, but much more information is available.

When humans are described as aggressive, the pejorative tone is almost always present, and there is a vast body of evidence on the determination of aggression as a set of human behavioural states. Veroude *et al.* (2016) summarise evidence on the inheritance of these states. Heritability of variously defined forms of aggression lies between 0.2 and 0.9, common environmental effects between 0 and 0.3 and general environmental effects between 0.1 and 0.6. Heritability, the proportion of additive genetical variance in the total phenotypic variance, is that part of the variance generally available for phenotypic directional selection (Fisher, 1999), so the reasons for so much additive variance have been sought in speculation about human evolutionary history, e.g. that aggression was

useful when humans were evolving in small bands or tribes, and in the likely pleiotropic effects of genes influencing behaviour. (As noted already, variance in fitness traits is not, of course, expected to disappear under directional selection e.g. Mayo *et al.* 1990.) Long-term selection experiments in plants and animals show that response can continue long after the initial V_A is exhausted (e.g. Mayo 1987).

There is also significant evidence of interaction between genotype and environment in determining whether a phenotype is described as aggressive or not (Tuvblad and Baker 2011; Veroude *et al.* (2016). In this context, Tremblay (2010) asserted that disruptive behaviour is normal behaviour in the infant and that sociable behaviour is learned, so that when disruptive behaviour manifests itself in later life as aggression, this is as a result of normal development itself being distorted or disrupted. He noted that philosophers had long considered this question of 'original sin' before Darwin provided the evolutionary explanation. Furthermore, Tremblay assessed the evidence as pointing to some types of disruptive behaviour being epigenetically influenced. He concludes that intervention, starting early in pregnancy will 'advance knowledge on causes and prevention of' disruptive behaviour. The knowledge so gained would also contribute to an understanding of aggression. It will be of interest to learn what are the underlying molecular mechanisms, and in particular what parts of these complex phenotypes have evolved in which species. (It is not only genomics that will be useful; brain-imaging has promise (Hazlett *et al.*, 2017; Blokland *et al.*, 2011), but is not relevant to this aspect of 'original sin'.)

3.12.5 Sloth

Guyau (1885, book 1, chapter 1) held that sloth was the worst vice, from an evolutionary point of view, mainly because action is the key to evolution. This view of action perhaps caused Guyau to hold that the highest virtues were those involved in sociability. On this interpretation, natural selection might be expected to minimise sloth unless there were particular circumstances in which it became advantageous.

Sloth may permit the avoidance of inappropriate action. Gustavson *et al.* (2014) found the heritability of procrastination, an element of slothfulness, to be 0.46. In the same study, they found that the heritability of 'impulsivity' (impulsiveness, temerity) to be 0.49 and the genetic correlation between the two traits to be 1.00. (A genetic correlation can be regarded as an estimate of the additive genetic effect that is common to two traits.) They considered that 'goal-managing ability underlies the genetic commonality between procrastination and impulsivity' (p. 1184). Elaborating this, 'procrastinators are also impulsive in large part because they fail to manage goals effectively to guide their behaviours' (p. 1186). The tendency to inactivity that may be the better part of sloth is not encompassed in this assessment.

Basal metabolic rate is heritable, for example heritable is about 0.4 in common rats (Sadowska *et al.* 2005). It is 0.25 in the zebra finch *Taeniopygia guttata*, according to Rønning *et al.* (2007), although this is strongly genetically correlated with body size, which has a high heritability. Careau *et al.* (2008) conclude that behaviour and BMR are likely to be highly correlated, and that behavioural phenotype in regard to activity and arousal is likely to be positively correlated with BMR. In this case, placidity might represent the other aspect of sloth.

Extreme inactivity could be advantageous in extreme environmental conditions, through reduction of energy use. This might be particularly the case for small heterothermic mammals, that is ones exhibiting characteristics of both poikilothermy and homoeothermy. Nowack et al. (2015) studied Australian sugar gliders *Petaurus breviceps* in a coastal environment seasonally prone to storms. They are heterothermic and can become torpid in conditions of poor food supply. Nowack *et al.* found that the gliders did indeed take shelter and become inactive to the point of torpor during storms, resuming normal activity in subsequent clement weather.

It is evident that both contributors to sloth, that is resting level of activity and tendency to act without reflection, could be advantageous or disadvantageous under different circumstances, as in the glider example, and that neither offers any guide as to the avoidance of sloth and its consequences.

3.12.6 Gluttony

Gluttony is manifested in eating past satiety and perhaps in having a very high threshold of satiety relative to capacity. The narrow sense heritability of satiety threshold in a wolf spider *Schizocosa acreata* is greater than 0.5. Animals with a high threshold produce larger egg masses and more offspring, but are at greater risk of predation, which may mean that the trait has a centralising tendency, overall, and the high genetical opportunity of selective change does not result in such change. It is not known whether human gluttony is related to the satiety threshold or indeed whether it is determined in the same way, and hence whether the spider's behaviour genetics is relevant.

In humans, appetite has heritability greater than 0.5 and appears to increase with age, but genotype-environment interactions are not easy to disentangle (Wardle and Carnell, 2009). These authors note that 'the "obese" are [not] a distinct group' and that '"obesogenic" environmental pressures [do not] have a similar effect on everyone'; the higher the body mass index (BMI = mass (in kg)/height (in m^2)), the higher the response to such pressures.

We can conclude that appetite has value for survival, and normal variation will, under conditions of easy availability of food and absence of necessary exercise, lead to excessive intake which may appear to be gluttony but may simply reflect absence of cues to limit that intake or inappropriate response to false cues in the environment.

3.12.6.1 Addiction

Addiction is an example of a class of behaviours, viz. normal behaviour taken to excess, according to some external judgement.

Consider the 'admittedly serious question of alcohol – only very extensive and authoritative experiment will suffice to show mankind whether it is a wise and healthy thing to take it in small quantities, the exact limits of which must be stated, or to reject it altogether'. (Lankester 1907, p. 40) The research has been done. We have an idea of how little alcohol must be consumed to do no harm. It is rather small, though probably not zero, and there may be modest benefits to low consumption (e.g. Letenneur 2004). We know that banning can work, after a fashion, when a society agrees, as in Saudi Arabia, and how it cannot work if society is divided, as in the USA under Prohibition.

3.12.7 Jealousy and envy

Confronted with unacceptable behaviour by another man towards a woman close to him, a man becomes angry, first at the other man, then at the woman. One could say, as Harris (op. cit., p. 73) does in a similar example, that jealousy arises as if one's 'inner ape had swung into view'. As noted, particularly in regard to spite, similar behaviour in other species may not be the same behaviour. What might be called civilisation by those who practise it has in some cases suppressed this behaviour, and it seems possible that natural selection for self-control has occurred, since some level thereof is necessary for a community of social animals not to tear itself apart. There is evidence for genetical variability in self-control (e.g. Yancey *et al.*, 2013), which as always supports the possibility of natural selection.

Thornhill and Palmer (2000, p. 42) assert that jealousy evolved from the need by males to believe that they are the fathers of their partners' children. There is no direct evidence for this proposition. The empirical finding that self-reported jealously experienced by females differs from that experienced by males is relevant, but DeSteno and Salovey (1996), who have described this work, caution against any evolutionary interpretation. Yoshimura (2010) reported that envy was more frequent amongst siblings than amongst siblings-in-law, which may be interpreted as evidence against Thornhill and Palmer's assertion.

Jealousy and envy are closely related, but the former may involve three parties whereas the latter requires only two. Distinction of the two is needed for genetical analysis (Parrott and Smith 1993). Dissection of their genetics has not been widely attempted.

3.12.7.1 'Spite' in other animals than humans

Spite is often recognised in human affairs, though others' motives are not always clear. Aesop's fables of the farmer and the viper and the frog and the mouse attribute malice or spite to animals other than humans, in classic anthropomorphic style, but it was not until the work of Price (1970) and Hamilton (1970) that a plausible evolutionary model of spite was proposed.

Hamilton (1970, p. 1219) wrote: 'Behaviour which harms others without benefit to the self may well be called "spiteful".' Following Price, he presented a very simple genetical model which allowed something like 'spite' to evolve. He noted three examples, from birds and insects (one social insect, one not) that might have other explanations through advantage to the perpetrator of the apparently spiteful act. The third example, of a maize pest (earworm *Heliothis zea*), is particularly striking: Hamilton, quoting another worker, wrote that the first grub 'to establish itself inside an ear of maize "... usually eats all subsequent arrivals. It is very uncommon for more than one earworm to survive in each cob although the food would be sufficient for 2 or more"'. Hamilton considered that the apparent rarity of true spite probably arose through the fact that every act has a cost. Natural selection tends to minimise costs, among other directional changes.

For spiteful behaviour to evolve by natural selection, relatedness ρ in Hamilton's inequality must be negative i.e. the interacting individuals must be less likely than randomly chosen individuals to be carrying genes that are identical by descent.

Foster *et al.* (2001) took the argument much further, and identified thirteen cases, mostly in vertebrate species, in which apparently spiteful individuals gain a benefit from their 'spiteful' act. They also considered three cases where spite was more likely to be present, including one in which negative relatedness was established in which 'spite' was mediated by recognition of the product of a single gene.

Schadenfreude is closely related to spite, but not easy to identify in other species, since our insight into their mental processes is not mediated by language.

3.13 Genetical defects

Multicellular organisms have a life-cycle, which requires replication of germ cells, combination of germ cells, and then development of a new organism. Single-celled organisms replicate themselves by cell division. Every cell division contains the possibility of mistakes in copying the genetical material, whether RNA or DNA. Although replication has itself evolved to be protected by error-correcting mechanisms, such mechanisms have a non-zero probability of failing to correct all errors, so that some errors must creep in. Some of these errors manifest themselves in changed phenotypes, some do not, but genetically caused defects occur all the time. They are entirely understandable on an evolutionary basis.

It is not possible to prevent all genetical defects. Some new dominant conditions arise as fresh germline mutations, for example. 'Personalised medicine', whereby individuals' genomes are characterised fully, could allow couples to avoid some recessive defects, but for every early pregnancy to be checked, several revolutions in costing and ease of testing would be needed. The outcomes could

be eugenic or dysgenic, according to what means were used and according to one's view of diversity.

3.13.1 'Hopeful monsters'

Every major evolutionary divergence must by definition start with something out of the ordinary, be it an environmental change that reveals previously suppressed variation, an environmental change that makes previously advantageous phenotypes disadvantageous, a mutation that allows its bearer to exploit an unchanged environment better, or some other immediately or potentially disruptive change. Canalisation is the propensity to resist environmental shocks in development (Waddington, 1957). It is the developmental analogue of homoeostasis in the normal adult animal. It has been demonstrated to be breakable by extreme environmental conditions, with hidden genetical variability revealed, for example in selection experiments in *Drosophila melanogaster* or increased egg-laying in poultry (Rendel, 1967). Over-population or an ice age's onset could be examples of the kind of environmental change that would break canalisation down.

The change in phenotype, whatever its cause, need not be large: a looser pelt on an arboreal mammal that allowed bigger wind resistance might have been the first step towards flight in that lineage, just as might have been longer inter-joint distances in the limbs.

Such small changes would work, but so would larger ones: the hopeful monsters. Attitudes towards monsters, that is to say organisms differing greatly from their parents in an unexpected way, have included the idea that they show a way forward. For example, Paul wrote (1809, p. 49): 'Do not tell me that congenital abnormalities arise against nature; each must be natural, otherwise it could not have come into existence; and do we know in any case which hidden organic error or exaggeration of your or my existence will finally pass to eternity? All life, even if it lasts only a moment, has eternal laws behind it; and a monster is simply a simultaneous statute-book of a federation of tiny body-part states; further, the most irregular form develops according to most regular laws (irregular rules are senseless).'

These were defined by Goldschmidt as macromutations that had the potential to be saltations, in Darwin's words, and lead to innovation in evolution of a kind that Otto Schindewolf and Richard Goldschmidt considered Darwinian natural selection (as they understood it) to be incapable of.

The case of Schindewolf is instructive. He was a palaeontologist concerned with the evolution of ammonites and corals. He developed a set of 'laws' of evolution that governed the flowering and dying out of species over geological time. He posited that there had been sudden changes in lineages following macromutations in Goldschmidt's sense. He produced an elegant hypothesis for the origin of birds from reptiles. To explain the absence of intermediate forms in the fossil record, he preferred evolution by saltation to the imperfections in that record cited by Darwin.

A recent example has been claimed in shepherd's purse *Capsella bursa-pastoris* by Hintz *et al.* (2006).

Do these 'monsters' claim privileges for mutants? Should we treat human mutants differently because they may be augurs of superhuman change?

3.14 Chomsky's theory of language: a single mutation, not something that evolved

What might we want to explain? As noted already, some aspects of ethics, such as identification of particular 'sins' or infractions of some implicit code seem to require language. Racialism or xenophobia or poujadism may or may not have a biological component in their determination, but require language for exposition. As Childe (1926, cited in Green 1981, p. 54) wrote: 'Words are the very stuff of thought. It follows then that a common language does imply a common mental attitude in its speakers; it not only reflects but also conditions ways of thinking peculiar to the users of the tongue in question.' This implies that much behaviour is conditioned on language and the idea that language arose at a stroke, so to speak, is critical for the assessment of the biological component of behaviour.

Chomsky wrote 'the evolution of language into its modern form could have consisted entirely in a single mutation in a single individual – a mutation that allowed a human to construct complex thoughts.' [In a footnote, Chomsky added 'human concepts were in place well before this'.] Taking this further, he wrote 'A single step would suffice … assuming that conceptual (thought) systems and articulatory and perceptual systems were in place' (Chomsky and McGilvray 2012, p. 176). Separation of speech, language and conceptual thought is not easy. The development of language required at least conceptual thought, individual learning, cultural transmission and biological evolution, and all of these appear to be found in non-human species. Cultural transmission to each new language user, through one-to-one, many-to-one and many-to-many transactions, is an essential for any particular language, whatever may be the biological structures underlying language as a whole.

As the molecular clock, probably renamed the genomic clock, becomes more precise, and perhaps all-encompassing, the question of how many mutations language 'required' to come into existence will be resolved. Then the question of what behaviours require language for manifestation may be resolved. Meanwhile, we can consider the claimed uniqueness of human language.

If language, including previously thought to be unique properties such as recursion, is not unique to humans, its role as source of 'humanness' is brought into question. The further from unique we are, the less can we justify appeals to uniqueness to justify particular behaviour. Gagliano and Grimonprez (2015) argue that most of the defining attributes of language are to be found in plant communication. They further argue than an understanding of the non-uniqueness of human language and of the nature of plant language, yielding 'an embodied conception of language could offer a valuable step towards the de-objectification of plants and the recognition of their subjectivity [sic] and inherent worth and dignity, renewing a sense of ecological intimacy and kinship with these nonhuman living *others* and thus promoting human care for nature' (p. 150). This worthy goal has only been reached by bringing ethics in from the outside; it does not inhere in the argument. Accepting the argument, one would find that many practices taken for granted (e.g. clonal orchards or vineyards) are inherently unethical.

3.15 Eugenics

That all babies shall be 'well born' in the sense of having loving parents, a healthy gestation and a healthy outlook at birth is a reasonable hope. Indeed, as Fraser (1976) pointed out, this comes from the Universal Declaration of Human Rights. Eugenics as a social movement directed towards improvement of the human gene pool has of course largely fallen into desuetude as a result of the grotesque abuses of the twentieth century. It continues to be discussed, as mentioned in section 2.5 above, and advocated (e.g. Hartung in the discussion to Vining (1986) or Savulescu *et al.*, 2011). Gene editing and pre-implantation genetic diagnosis will probably make eugenics a policy issue once more (e.g. Cyranoski 2017) but the ethical issue, usually addressed through utility or revelation, has not been solved by evolutionary findings, and is discussed further below.

What means are chosen to ensure this goal are open to discussion. Genetic counselling is one such means. It is usually intended to have a eugenic effect in the short term, but can have eugenic or dysgenic effects in the longer term, as discussed by Mayo (1972, pp. 56–57).

Genetical testing, at whatever stage of life, is necessary for counselling, and it has raised ethical dilemmas in relation to distressing and incurable conditions such as Huntington's disease and Alzheimer's disease (AD): is it better to know or not to know; is it better to advise or not to advise? Van Cauwenberghe et al. (2016) have said that 'testing [for a particular probabilistic risk factor for AD] in at-risk individuals with a positive family history does not pose significant psychological risks like depression or anxiety when they are provided by proper pre- and post-test counselling' (p. 427). Is this true in all communities? Is it justified for a relative risk less than 4?

'Therapeutic abortion' is used as a consequence of genetic counselling and otherwise. Fraser (1976) wrote that in considering prevention of hereditary diseases, we use the word prevention in an unusual sense. There is a striking antithesis when we talk of 'therapeutic abortion'. We prevent tuberculosis by stopping the development of the disease, not by killing the patient.[1] It is clear that the problem is one of ends and means. The end is the prevention of the birth of a child with a particular genotype. The means is destruction of a foetus. This is not unusual biologically; a high proportion of all conceptions ends naturally in the destruction of the embryo at an early stage (15–50%, Rai and Regan 2006). A smaller proportion of conceptuses is lost at later stages.

Care of oneself as a potential parent is a need for a healthy child to be born. This may be said to be an ethical imperative, but only on Kantian or other religious grounds. Even if this were accepted, implementation could involve coercion. Knowledge of the causation of, for example, fetal alcohol syndrome may not be held by those most at risk. The same applies to the hazards of tobacco smoke (e.g. Slotkin *et al.*, 2017).

---

[1] 'Quand nous parlons de prévention des maladies héréditaires, nous utilisons ce mot dans un sens inhabituel. Il nous fournit une antithèse assez frappante quant aux considérations thérapeutiques dont on vient de parler. En effet, nous ne prévenons la tuberculose en empêchant la conception du malade, et non plus en le tuant.' (Fraser 1976)

3.16 Xenophobia and abjection

The heritability of xenophobia, or something like it, is low (Martin *et al.* 1986). Further, males and females are discordant, females showing largely cultural transmission of attitude, males weak genetical transmission. Change under natural selection could have occurred, but we do not know, for example, whether there has been recent secular change over time, indicating environmental not genetical change.

Speculation over the origin of xenophobia cannot alter the fact that it occurs. Furthermore, it probably fluctuates in frequency and intensity over time. It is seen in ancient religious texts and in statements of present-day politicians. These same texts can be the source of belief in the imperfection and fall of man (Brunetière par. 5 below; though Brunetière himself, the case of Dreyfus aside, was not in his own assessment racist: Brunetière 1913, pp. 44–7).

There is now increasing evidence of the importance of assortative mating in 'the genomic architecture of traits in humans' (Robinson *et al.* 2017, p. 1). In this study, a solid genetic correlation between partners was confirmed for educational attainment, height, blood pressure and various measures of body size. The genetic correlations were conformable with but not identical to the phenotypic correlations between partners. This study was based on trait-associated loci, and is almost entirely free of environmental influences. The fundamental tendency to prefer similarity that these results indicate must exist may lie beneath many tendencies towards distrust of 'the other'.

Haslam and Loughnan (2014) have shown just how broad can be the pernicious behaviour resulting from racialist thought, which could contribute to the low heritability and the strong possibility of environmental modification, for good or ill.

3.17 Equity

McAuliffe *et al.* (2017) have claimed that 'the signatures of human fairness can be traced into childhood. Children make sacrifices for fairness

(1) when they have less than others, (2) when others have been unfair and (3) when they have more than others.' They makes this claim on the basis of extensive neurobiological evidence. According to the evidence they review, there appears to be some support for the idea that fairness is innate, though development of a range of behaviours is necessary for fairness to be made manifest.

Brunetière, par. 3 and 29, 1894 appealed to fairness, using the concept in an unexamined way, i.e. as if it was obvious that it should be used and how it should be used. It is certainly a fundamental concept in human affairs, whether unique to humans, as McAuliffe *et al.* (2017) claim, or not. It underlies a huge range of dealings. When Ruskin (1860) wrote 'Whereas it has long been known and declared that the poor have no right to the property of the rich, I wish it also to be known and declared that the rich have no right to the property of the poor.', he was appealing to fairness, but did not need to say so.

If fairness is 'built in', then it may drive 'ought' without the need for ratiocination, but this does not solve Hume's problem. Furthermore, 'built in' fairness has not been successful throughout history, so its strength is questionable.

3.18 Reproduction

Reproduction requires, in most cases, co-operation, active in animals, not necessarily active in plants and other orders. Such co-operation may have been very important in the evolution of workable social behaviour in populations no longer small. It is a topic loaded with preconceptions, hard to discuss with any hope of objectivity. As Haldane (1932, pp. 20–21) wrote:

> Human physiology is indecent. To take a simple example, it would be ridiculous to frame a practical course of that science which did not involve the analysis of urine, or a theoretical course which omitted the physiology of reproduction.

Most people desire that thought on the latter subject should remain in the pre-scientific stage, and heavily charged with emotion. The emotion may vary in different cases. Some find it a subject for sentimentality, others for disgust, others, again, for humour. All agree in fearing an objective and scientific attitude to it, though this fear is rationalized in a number of different ways. As a consequence a considerable proportion of the rising generation is adopting a purely hedonistic standpoint on this topic. I think that those who are conservative in this matter should realize that, from their point of view, a biological attitude is preferable to a hedonistic. The biologist, for example, generally finds it improbable that a woman should find satisfaction in permanently interrupting the normal reproductive cycle so as to omit pregnancy and lactation, even though a low infantile mortality necessitates a certain degree of interference on social grounds.

Although Haldane exhibits some of the (unconscious) biases he warns against, and although scientific advances and other developments have changed how, for example, people can approach hedonism, the key point is that drawing ethical inferences from biology is almost impossible in the sphere of sexual behaviour and physiology. The attempt to 'explain' rape in evolutionary terms is perhaps the best example (section 2.5 above).

3.18.1 Non-breeding behaviour

The choice not to reproduce, whether through 'orthosexual' ('heteronormative') decision or 'parasexual' modus vivendi, is in a society like 21st century Australia mostly a conscious choice. I have already cited Fisher and Haldane on the subject. At a larger level of aggregation, nations can influence family size, as shown in recent decades in China, and individual decisions will be taken within whatever societal

context surrounds those considering reproduction. The question of free will I have discussed at length, but take its existence for granted in this context.

The choice not to breed has behavioural consequences. For example, child-rearing by non-breeders may have a different intellectual context, to say the least, and may affect many choices and much behaviour.

Harris (2010, p. 239) wrote:

> What would it mean for a couple to decide that they *should* have a child? It probably means that they think that their own well-being will tend to increase for having brought another person into the world; it should also mean that they expect their child to have a life that is, on balance, worth living. If they didn't expect these things, it's hard to see why they would want to have a child in the first place.
>
> However, most of the research done on happiness suggests that people actually become less happy when they have children and do not begin to approach their prior level of happiness until their children leave home… Let us say that you are aware of this research but imagine that you will be an exception. Of course, another body of research shows that most people think that they are exceptions to rules of this sort: there is almost nothing more common that the belief that one is above average in intelligence, wisdom, honesty etc. But you are aware of this research as well, and it does not faze you. Perhaps, in your case, all relevant exceptions are true, and you will be precisely as happy a parent as you hope to be. However, a famous study of human achievement suggests that one of the most reliable ways to diminish a person's contributions to society is for that person to start a family… How would you view your decision to have a child if you knew

that all the time you spent changing diapers and playing with Lego would prevent you from developing the cure for Alzheimer's disease that was actually within your reach?

On Harris's argument, couples, by having children, are not maximising their happiness (substituted without comment for well-being) or even the probability of achieving greater well-being. However, this relies on happiness (or well-being) being an instantaneous, evanescent state, existing in the shortest of short-terms. The facts that planning for the future takes place and that people undertake activities now that provide benefits later tend to disprove this part of Harris's argument. (His argument also ignores the 'contribution to society' that having a child represents, but that is another story.)

It is not as if this aspect of behaviour is rare. Dr Johnson famously said, on 19 September 1777 (Boswell 1872), 'If I had no duties and no reference to futurity, I would spend my life in driving briskly in a post-chaise with a pretty woman; but she should be one who could understand me, and would add something to the conversation.' Even here, the future is important, and is not discounted to zero, as in Harris's argument.

If our will is not free, as Harris (op. cit., pp. 135–40 and elsewhere) argues ('A voluntary action is accompanied by the felt intention to carry it out, while an involuntary action isn't.', pp. 139–40.), then the decision to have a child probably depends more than many on basic biology. However, Lawson and Borgerhoff Mulder (2016) claim that, 'while the optimization of [human organism] quantity trade-offs undoubtedly shaped the evolution of human physiology setting the upper limits of reproduction, … it plays a modest role in accounting for socio-ecological and individual variation in human fertility.' That is, in societies with education and contraception widely available, other factors than biology have become important. This, of course, was

the basis of Fisher's (1999) advocacy of family allowances for the children of the demonstrably intelligent. It was a normative argument based on observed differences in the achieved fertility of different classes, before easily effective contraception was available. It is not clear that one can conclude, with Lawson and Mulder that 'there is also a need for greater attention to the possibility that sexual conflict may influence fertility optima in certain contexts.' Domestic violence, to take one example of 'sexual conflict', should be stopped, regardless of its present or past evolutionary role: this is a normative statement based on being human.

The heritability of human fertility, given the constraints just discussed and others considered by Mayo *et al.* (1973) and many others, is quite low (0.1–0.2, Smith 1975). There is, however, enormous variability, and the opportunity for change under natural selection is large.

3.19 Waste

The word connotes disapproval, yet waste is normal. It is central to evolution by natural selection. One of the most frequently quoted sentences of Malthus (1798, p. 17) is: 'The prodigious waste of human life occasioned by this perpetual struggle for room and food, was more than supplied by the mighty power of population, acting, in some degree, unshackled, from the constant habit of emigration.' Darwin took this loss into consideration in formulating his theory, but recognised the necessity of death as part of life.

Waste is the result of life, both at the level of death and at the more general level of the use of energy by living organisms: this must obey the second law of thermodynamics. Organisms build up information by the use of energy, but some of the energy is dissipated. When organisms die, other organisms use that built-up information, the compounds of which the dead organism is composed, for their own purposes. From the careful phosphorus house-keeping of any plant evolved on Australia's impoverished soils (e.g. Handreck 1997) to the bone-eating worms in the deep ocean that take advantage of occasional dead whales (Rouse *et al.* 2004), organisms have appeared through natural selection to take advantage of whatever captured information is available.

Properly understood, that is to say, seen from other than an anthropocentric standpoint, waste is not what is being generated by life.

3.20 Parasitism

Parasitism is ubiquitous in living matter, found at all levels of biological organisation, from sub-organismal (Gogarten and Hilario 2006) to complex eukaryotes. When a host organism is driven to extinction, the loss of genetical information in its obligate parasites is greater that the host's (Dunn *et al.*, 2009): 'It remains conceivable that coextinction is the most common form of extinction. It is also possible, however, that many parasites and mutualists are more resistant to the loss of their hosts or partners than is immediately apparent'. Dunn *et al.* point to various possibilities, such as host change, that could lead to this mitigation of extinction.

Knowledge of the ubiquity of parasitism and the non-existent boundary between parasitism and mutualism might be expected to engender less extreme hostility to parasitism, but this is to have the right to expect such a change. Dunn *et al.* specifically ask, 'why should we care?' and answer that extinction of parasites will cause 'loss of biological diversity and diversification', 'loss of history' and 'loss of traits'. In this last case, 'If coextinctions are phylogenetically clustered, it is likely that coextinction will produce non-random loss of traits. One can imagine a suite of parasite and mutualist traits (other than host specificity) that might be at greater risk of loss during coextinctions.' On a utilitarian argument, 'should' here means a potential lost benefit to some unspecified entity, such as the whole of humanity, but it still argues from 'is' to 'ought'.

3.21 Laughter

Many curious discussions have been written on the causes of laughter with grown-up persons. The subject is extremely complex. Something incongruous or unaccountable, exciting surprise and some sense of superiority in the laugher, who must be in a happy frame of mind, seems to be the commonest cause... The circumstances must not be of a momentous nature: no poor man would laugh or smile on suddenly hearing that a large fortune had been bequeathed to him. If the mind is strongly excited by pleasurable feelings, and any little unexpected event or thought occurs, then, as Mr. Herbert Spencer remarks ... "a large amount of nervous energy, instead of being allowed to expend itself in producing an equivalent amount of the new thoughts and emotion which were nascent, is suddenly checked in its flow."..."The excess must discharge itself in some other direction, and there results an efflux through the motor nerves to various classes of the muscles, producing the half-convulsive actions we term laughter." An observation, bearing on this point, was made by a correspondent during the recent siege of Paris, namely, that the German soldiers, after strong excitement from exposure to extreme danger, were particularly apt to burst out into loud laughter at the smallest joke. (Darwin 1872, p. 200)

The origin of laughter, Darwin speculated, was in the expression of joy and related feelings, and he drew on wide observation of other primates in particular to indicate that it had evolved. He also drew attention to the fact that the baring of teeth, which has other expressive functions, could have been enlisted into the expression of joy.

It is not necessary that Darwin was right to see how important laughter is as an outcome of human development. Brunetière used wit, sarcasm, irony and other aspects of humour to drive his argument forward, but did not address laughter itself as part of the evolved human condition.

3.22 Immortality

We do not need to explain immortality: 'to live knowing that life in pointless is what gives rise to anguish' (Camus, 1989, p. 168). 'Man should believe in immortality; he has a right to this belief; it corresponds with the wants of his nature, and he may believe in the promises of religion. But if the philosopher tries to deduce the immortality of the soul from a legend [e.g. the resurrection], that is very weak and inefficient. To me, the eternal existence of my soul is proved from my idea of activity; if I work on incessantly till my death, nature is bound to give me another form of existence when the present one can no longer sustain my spirit.'(Goethe 1850, p. 122) Without necessarily agreeing with Goethe, one can recognise that it lies outside the realm of sensory perception. For example, Barnes (1924, p. 147) wrote

> The belief that human personality survives the dissolution of the body is neither confirmed nor discredited by 'natural science'. There is no direct conclusive evidence for the existence of consciousness apart from life, or for the existence of life apart from matter. All our knowledge negatives the fancies of transmigration [of souls] and re-incarnation. Belief in human immortality rests

on a metaphysical basis. It is a corollary from the acceptance of ethical theism. Natural science only affects the belief in so far as it affects our spiritual interpretation of the universe. But ethical theism is the one satisfactory interpretation which we can reach when we attempt to give unity, not only to conceptions derived from the physical and biological sciences, but also to those which we derive from the study of human consciousness.

For a good account of arguments against immortality, see those presented by Guyau (1885) in the course of his attempt to build a Hume-free, evolution-independent secular ethics. He held the view that hope for indefinitely prolonged life builds belief in immortality, and that there was no formal basis for this hope.

As Brunetière respected Huxley, I shall leave the last word on the topic to the latter (Huxley 1894d, p. 210):

> ...nothing [in Kant's opinion] can be proved or disproved respecting either the distinct existence, the substance, or the durability of the soul. So far, Kant is at one with Hume. But Kant adds, as you cannot disprove the immortality of the soul, and as the belief therein is very useful for moral purposes, you may assume it. To which, had Hume lived half a century later, he would probably have replied, that, if morality has no better foundation than an assumption, it is not likely to bear much strain; and, if it has a better foundation, the assumption rather weakens than strengthens it.

4 Lessons

Brunetière (par. 36) held that the study of evolution by natural selection had transformed philosophy as much as science and, with this in mind, that he was simply 'considering some consequences of the theory'. Following him, I have done the same, in regard to the outcomes of research that might be said to impinge on human ethics.

4.1 The Fall

According to Andrews (2015, p, 258), the last common ancestor of present-day humans and chimpanzees, some 5 to 8 million years ago, had the following characteristics: opportunistic omnivory, with meat socially important but not a large dietary component, but probably no scavenging; low reproductive rate, like present-day apes; tool-making for a wide range of purposes, differing between regions, but not making tools for making tools; re-use of artefacts; compound artefacts rare; transport of raw materials and tools over short distances; greater manual dexterity than chimpanzees; complex nest-building in trees, for security, but possibly also permitting establishment of home bases; nomadic over large regions, subject to availability of water, trees for nests and fig trees for food. These conclusions are drawn from a study of the fossil record, DNA, and the ecology and ethology of apes and humans. When we consider what has happened in human evolution since that divergence, viz. development of the human brain, development of language and the use of fire and other complex tools, we can say that the 'descent of man' has not been a steep fall in capability, even if it has been a fall from grace.

Religions have much to say about choice of partner, and some of these sayings relate to the avoidance of close inbreeding, which is generally risky in biological terms. What any given religion or set of customs prescribes or proscribes can vary a great deal. For example, in Tamil Nadu in a rural community, Rao *et al.* 1972) found relatively close consanguinity of 49% in 8889 rural marriages, of which over 35% were uncle-niece marriages. In an urban setting comparable in other ways, the overall consanguinity was slightly over 29%, of which 24% were uncle-niece. The rural-urban change appeared to mediate a reduction in consanguinity, yet the overall rates remained remarkably high compared with, say, Australia.

Darwin (1871/1901) considered the likely behaviour of small bands of early 'humans' on the basis of comparison with other species of ape, and concluded that leadership of a band by a dominant male would lead to control of sexual behaviour and also to the extrusion from the band of young males, so that exogamy would be forced on them. Approving, Freud (e.g. Freud 1956, p. 130) considered that this would have been the origin of systematic control of sexuality and the incest prohibition. Thus, part of some religions would have come out of the evolution of behaviour, whether social or biological. This links some further aspects of the Fall with what appears to have happened over time.

The time-scale for evolution is of course much longer than described for the Fall in sacred texts. Brunetière does not mention time, in this sense. Accordingly, it seems appropriate to use the longer time-scale. Current 'dysgenic' and 'dysphenic' human activities, from maternity at age 70 to 'therapeutic abortion' of recessive homozygotes with consequent slowly increasing frequency of the recessive gene, are occurring on the shorter time-scale. Most of humanity does not yet have access to the tests involved in such genetical change, but selective abortion of female fetuses is having large-scale effects on the breeding populations of some populous countries. What these effects will be is not yet known. In any case, larger human activities, such as the production of climate change, may render considerations of microevolutionary change irrelevant.

Brunetière's acceptance of the Fall did not mean that he rejected the search for knowledge contained in the metaphor of eating the forbidden fruit, but he recognised the problems knowledge brings (e.g. pars 6 and 13).

What did Brunetière think, in summary, about ethics that could be derived from evolution? He concluded that evolution by natural selection accounted for the Fall of Man, and hence for redemption by a saviour, which in turn entailed the ethics of that saviour's belief system. In this light, 'love thy neighbour as thyself' (e.g. *Leviticus* 19:18 or *Matthew* 23:39) and all its consequences flow and are mandatory; they are revealed in the Testaments. Thus, a whole code of ethics is derived from evolution by natural selection and revelation. If one removes revelation, what remains is not clear.

4.2 'Original sin'

Brunetière considered that evolutionary theory explained the occurrence of original sin. To quote from him (below, par. 4):

> 'The differences in structure between man and the primates that resemble us most' wrote Professor Huxley in the most recent French translation of *Man's Place in Nature*, 'these differences are no greater than those that exist between these last and the other members of the order of primates, of such a nature that, if one has reason to believe that all the primates, man excepted, come from a

single primitive stock, there is nothing in the structure of man that authorises us to assign to man a different origin'. This we admit willingly, without hesitation or reserve. Far from us the repugnance of ridiculous vanity! Yes, we have in us, in our blood, and, so to speak, we all have deep in our veins, something of the brutality, the lubricity, the ferocity of the gorilla or the orang-utan! Do we bring with us, besides, nascent seeds of some virtues? That's the question! and for my part I would rather be tempted to deny it: our 'qualities' alone seem natural to me, health, beauty, vigour, skill; all our 'virtues' seem acquired to me. But what we certainly find within us are the seeds of all our vices, – to start with those which we impute to the iniquity of our social institutions; – and what could there be more natural , I wish to say easier to explain if we are the present term of an infinite series of animal ancestors?

Huxley said that evolution by natural selection does not imply good, progress etc., and has as yet nothing to say about free will: his statement does not imply original sin, because sin is not a biological concept, but an ethical one.

'[Christianity is] the faith that launched point-blank her dart at the head of a lie – taught Original Sin, The corruption of Man's Heart.' (from Gold Hair: a legend of Pornic' by Robert Browning) Imperfection of humans is simple on the basis of natural selection, which works on the available material.

The story is set out in the Biblical book of *Genesis*:

> 1 Now the serpent was more subtil than any beast of the field which the LORD God had made. And he said unto the woman, Yea, hath God said, Ye shall not eat of every tree of the garden? 2 And the woman said unto the serpent, We may eat of the fruit of the trees of the garden: 3 But of the fruit of the tree which is in the midst of the garden, God hath

said, Ye shall not eat of it, neither shall ye touch it, lest ye die. 4 And the serpent said unto the woman, Ye shall not surely die: 5 For God doth know that in the day ye eat thereof, then your eyes shall be opened, and ye shall be as gods, knowing good and evil. 6 And when the woman saw that the tree was good for food, and that it was pleasant to the eyes, and a tree to be desired to make one wise, she took of the fruit thereof, and did eat, and gave also unto her husband with her; and he did eat. 7 And the eyes of them both were opened, and they knew that they were naked; and they sewed fig leaves together, and made themselves aprons. 8 And they heard the voice of the LORD God walking in the garden in the cool of the day: and Adam and his wife hid themselves from the presence of the LORD God amongst the trees of the garden. 9 And the LORD God called unto Adam, and said unto him, Where art thou? 10 And he said, I heard thy voice in the garden, and I was afraid, because I was naked; and I hid myself. 11 And he said, Who told thee that thou wast naked? Hast thou eaten of the tree, whereof I commanded thee that thou shouldest not eat? 12 And the man said, The woman whom thou gavest to be with me, she gave me of the tree, and I did eat. 13 And the LORD God said unto the woman, What is this that thou hast done? And the woman said, The serpent beguiled me, and I did eat. 14 And the LORD God said unto the serpent, Because thou hast done this, thou art cursed above all cattle, and above every beast of the field; upon thy belly shalt thou go, and dust shalt thou eat all the days of thy life: 15 And I will put enmity between thee and the woman, and between thy seed and her seed; it shall bruise thy head, and thou shalt bruise his heel. 16 Unto the woman he said, I will greatly multiply thy sorrow and thy conception; in sorrow thou shalt bring forth children; and thy desire shall be to thy husband, and he shall rule over thee. 17 And unto Adam he said, Because thou hast hearkened unto the voice of thy wife, and hast eaten of the tree, of which I commanded thee, saying, Thou shalt not eat of it: cursed is the ground for thy sake; in sorrow shalt thou eat of it all the days of thy life; 18 Thorns also and thistles shall it bring forth to thee; and thou shalt eat the herb of the field; 19 In the sweat of thy face shalt thou eat bread, till thou return unto the ground; for out of it wast thou taken: for dust thou art, and unto dust shalt thou return. 20 And Adam called his wife's name Eve; because she was the mother of all living. 21 Unto Adam also and to his wife did the LORD God make coats of skins, and clothed them. 22 And the LORD God said, Behold, the man is become as one of us, to know good and evil: and now, lest he put forth his hand, and take also of the tree of life, and eat, and live for ever: 23 Therefore the LORD God sent him forth from the garden of Eden, to till the ground from whence he was taken. 24 So he drove out the man; and he placed at the east of the garden of Eden Cherubims, and a flaming sword which turned every way, to keep the way of the tree of life.

The woman beguiled the man; the snake tempted the woman; the snake is a *deus ex machina*. The parable is appealing, but the content is simply that human imperfection, moral and otherwise, is older than the first human children.

4.3 How is it that we need Theodicy?

Macdonell (1924, p. 53) wrote of the Sānkhya tradition in Hinduism: 'The atheism of the system was defended by its adherents with the declaration that the origin of evil presents an insoluble problem to the theist, because a god who has created and rules the world could not possibly escape from the reproach of cruelty and injustice.' Whether this description is a travesty of something much more complex or a good simplification, it explains briefly the need for believers in any kind of personal god to explain the origin of evil.

A theist's position is well stated by Johnson (2014, p. 187):

> The theodicy project is a philosophical effort to construct a rational defence of God's goodness and power in a world where evils occur. It figures there are reasons for suffering rooted in the divine will, and assesses pain, suffering and death in such a way that they are reconciled with divine intent. The result is a somewhat satisfying intellectual system that justifies God by explaining reasons for suffering, making room for evils to exist in a logically meaningful world.

Johnson notes that this approach, which of course is still based on revelation, does not satisfy all theologians and philosophers. She herself expresses the opinion that 'suffering and death are too much of an enigma to submit to such logic'; this fits with Haldane's idea about human limitations mentioned earlier (section 1.1), but is a counsel of despair nevertheless.

When we stop original research, we start thinking about its importance in a broader context. This is not the same as looking up from the microscope and saying 'I see it all!', as many elderly scientists are said to do. It is having the time not to worry about results, data, analysis and so on, and therefore seeking something else to worry about in that time. It is in this spirit that explanations for the inexplicable are sought.

We have enough traits to produce any character, any character at all. We can see aspects of these traits in other organisms. We can judge the form and distribution of these traits and investigate whether they give rise beneficial outcomes for the species, in the sense of contributing to fitness. Yet we have a plague of people.

Gut bacteria can stimulate the production of serotonin (5-hydroxytriptamine) in the cells that line the gut. Ninety percent. of the body's serotonin is produced in these cells (Yano *et al.* 2015). Given the importance of serotonin for mood and many behavioural traits, what are the implications for mood and other aspects of the individual? Is our search for meaning in the universe partly driven by our gut bacteria? Given their extraordinary diversity (Lozupone *et al.* 2012), one cannot rule out such speculations.

Theodicy has produced great literature, for example *Candide*, Voltaire's response to Leibniz, but has it advanced beyond the book of Job?

4.4 Free will

Brunetière did not discuss free will, though as a (Roman) Catholic he accepted its reality; he used the concept elsewhere, without, of course, going to Pelagian extremes (see, e.g., Brunetière 1913, Irvine 1959). Similarly, Guyau accepted its existence and considered that it had evolved, though Brunetière does not mention this. Free will is relevant to the place of evolution by natural selection in ethics.

First, however, one should note that Brunetière accepted much of the role of the will in evolution as espoused by Lamarck (Brunetière par. 28 below) but not the idea of a vital force (par. 31 below). Bergson (1911) was another who held that evolution was creative not through selection among organisms but through the will of the organism. Evolution by natural selection is not deterministic, though it has often been taken to be so, and Bergson, following Lamarck in spirit, was reacting against this supposed determinism. Politzer (1947, p. 13) regarded Bergsonism as, at bottom, a 'scandalous artifice'. Fisher (1950, p. 20), more constructively, pointed out how Bergson's and other evolutionary theories descending from Lamarck, rely on a drive, an urge or a will, whereas natural selection is concerned with acts: natural selection works its effects by 'doing or dying'. It needs to be emphasised that there is no will, free or otherwise, involved in change by natural selection.

Huxley (1894c, p. 141) put the old, common-sensical idea of free will very well:

> ...with respect to the old riddle of the freedom of the will. In the only sense in which the word freedom is intelligible to me – that is to say, the absence of any restraint upon doing what one likes within certain limits – physical science gives no more reason for doubting it than the common sense of mankind does. And if physical science, in strengthening our belief in the universality of causation and abolishing chance as an absurdity, leads to the conclusion of determinism, it does no more than follow the track of consistent and logical thinkers in philosophy and in theology, before it existed or was thought of. Whoever accepts the universality of the law of causation as a dogma of philosophy, denies the existence of uncaused phenomena. And the essence of that which is improperly called the freewill doctrine is that, occasionally at any rate, human volition is self-caused, that is to say, not caused at all; for to cause oneself one must have anteceded oneself – which is, to say the least of it, difficult to imagine.

Huxley (L. Huxley, 1900, p. 231) also put the case for computational determinism clearly, in an 1861 letter to Herbert Spencer, citing 'a favourite problem' of William Tyndall's: 'Given the molecular forces in a mutton chop, deduce Hamlet or Faust therefrom.' Tyndall, wrote Huxley, was 'confident that the Physics of the Future will solve this easily.' In fact, the physics of the future has produced indeterminacy, which may have put computational determinism permanently out of reach, even if it is not the basis of something like free will (Penrose, 1989).

In mainstream philosophy, free will is generally regarded as being ruled out through its inability to be reconciled with either determinism or randomness, which are mutually exclusive and exhaustive possibilities. However, as already discussed, in a binary choice between two very similar possibilities, the outcome of a single trial will be essentially random, apart from any inbuilt cognitive biases. In this case, choice is close to random and probably far from deterministic.

From the neurophysiological work of Kornhuber & Deecke (1965) and Libet *et al.* (1983), it appears that the brain can initiate a volitional act unconsciously before the 'conscious person' consciously initiates the act. This might appear to rule out free will, in the sense of conscious decision-making, but does it mean that the act was determined at the unconscious level?

Suppose that free will does not exist; that our actions are in some sense determined. Does this mean predestination?

Suppose a person's behaviour is determined, not free. What does this mean? Let us use a well-known passage from *Beyond Freedom and Dignity* (p. 214) to illustrate what determinism might mean:

> An experimental analysis shifts the determination of behaviour from autonomous man to the environment—an environment responsible both for the evolution of the species and for the repertoire acquired by each member. Early versions of environmentalism were inadequate because they could not explain how the environment worked, and much seemed to be left for autonomous man to do. But environmental contingencies now take over functions once attributed to autonomous man, and certain questions arise. Is man then "abolished"? Certainly not as a species or as an individual achiever. It is the autonomous inner man who is abolished, and that is a step forward. But does man not then become merely a victim or passive observer of what is happening to him? He is indeed controlled by his environment,

but we must remember that it is an environment largely of his own making.

How does the environment control the person? Envisage a person who has to make a decision to carry out one of two actions based on his or her judgement of the difference between two very closely matched magnitudes. The decision goes according to which magnitude is larger. From research discussed elsewhere (section 2.3), we know that precision can be achieved in repeated trials, but that in any particular case the possibility of error is close to 50%. The person may be programmed by the environment to choose to decide in one way, but as long as the task is carried out faithfully, the outcome will be close to random. To what extent can we say that the outcome was determined? Far from being abolished as an 'absurdity', chance is a necessity in biology.

Consider a person entering a committee meeting determined to vote in a particular way on an agenda item. A straw poll is taken and she votes 'against'. Then there is extensive discussion and she realises that her first decision was based on incomplete and hence misleading information, and votes 'for'. In what sense can these opposite votes be taken to be involuntary? In asking these questions, I am not advocating or relying on situationism; the general position put by Revelle (1995, p. 304) appears reasonable:

> That people who share a similar upbringing are more similar than those who do not is obvious. Similarities based on linguistic and cultural background have never been denied. The utility of using individual differences in one situation to predict individual differences in another situation, however, has been hotly contested. Debates about the relative importance of situational versus individual causes of consistencies and differences dominated a disproportionate amount of the literature of the 1970s and 1980s but became less virulent as both sides developed more tolerance, became exhausted, or developed a richer understanding of the underlying issues.

In noting this viewpoint, I am of course not ignoring important changes in understanding of how common environment influences people (Eaves *et al.* 1989). Such influences, however, are not relevant to the question in hand, which relates to the person as she or he is, not how she grew that way.

Take as a more specific example the claimed effect of the serotonin transporter polymorphism (*5HTTLPR*, 5-hydroxytriptamine gene-linked polymorphic region) on behaviour. This polymorphism has two alleles, *s* and *l*. Caspi *et al.* (2003) claimed that young adult carriers of the *s* allele who suffered severe childhood abuse were more likely to develop depression than carriers of the *l* allele. Nguyen *et al.* (2015, p. 107) observed 'greater depressive symptom severity among individuals with the *s/s* genotype who reported a history of severe child abuse compared with those without [such] a history.' 'However, among individuals without a history of severe child abuse, [they] detected a trend in which [those of] *s/s* genotype had more favourable depressive symptom trajectories compared with *s/l* and *l/l*'. 'This suggests that the … polymorphism may be a marker of 'phenotypic plasticity' rather than 'vulnerability' in that *s/s* [homozygotes] appear to be the most susceptible to the negative effects of severe child abuse (i.e. increased depressive symptom severity) but also marginally more likely to benefit from the absence of a severe child abuse experience [although this effect was small]'. Serotonin is important in much behaviour, so it is not surprising that an individual serotonin-related genetical mechanism is associated with a behavioural trait, but of course the complex web of interactions is merely disturbed in this example. We have a strong interaction between genotype and environment, early experience influencing later behaviour, a plastic phenotype, and overlapping distributions of symptoms. To what extent can depressive symptoms be regarded as determined between or within individuals? Can anything general be inferred from it?

There is evidence that olfaction is a quantum phenomenon (Tirandaz *et al.*, 2017). If pheromones are important in some aspects of human behaviour, as seems to be the case (Logan 2015), and if the pheromones are sensed through olfaction, can behaviour be determined completely? Can it be neither the result of free will nor of determinism?

'Migratory restlessness (also known as *Zugunruhe*) is the seasonally occurring behaviour of caged migratory birds that is expressed by high locomotor activity during migration seasons and is considered to be an indicator of the urge for migration' (Sudo & Tsukamoto 2015, p. 1) It also occurs in other migratory animals. Sudo & Tsukamoto have suggested that in Japanese eels this phenomenon is triggered or enhanced by increased levels of an androgen (11-ketotestosterone). Changes in hormone levels trigger a wide range of phenomena in many animal species. If an individual is predisposed to a particular choice but a hormone pushes the choice in the opposite direction, then at some point in the range of choice, the individual may come to either decision with an intermediate frequency; is such a choice determined?

There is evidence that the brain responds faster to threatening images than to non-threatening images. Méndez-Bértolo *et al.* (2016, p. 1047) have written 'The existence of a subcortical route to the amygdala from rapid processing of ecologically important stimuli has markedly influence basic and clinical research on emotional processing in the brain.' They conclude that they have now demonstrated this: the human amygdala responds very rapidly to images of frightening faces but to those of neutral or comforting faces. Might this mean that decisions relating to avoidance are taken unconsciously faster than other decisions? There is evidence that impulsiveness in genetically variable (Fadel *et al.* 2016), so there could be variation in the speed of decision making, even among 'fast' and 'slow' decisions; would none be freely taken?

Again, it is known that 'the prefrontal cortex is responsible for emotional conflict resolution, and this control mechanism is affected by the emotional valence of distracting stimuli' (Yang *et al.* 2016, p. 1) and these authors have further

indicated that, as the DLPFC (dorsolateral prefrontal cortex) modulates emotional conflict control, there can be an 'emotional processing priority effect on conflict control from the cognitive domain to emotional domain' *ibid*, p. 6). Under such circumstances, will decisions always be the same as under non-distracting circumstances? What of the resting state (e.g. Bonnard *et al.*, 2016): what decisions are taken then?

Monti *et al.* (2013, p. 8) have suggested that 'changes in the level of consciousness induced by propofol affect basic organization principles and dynamics of information processing across the whole brain as well as within specific regions known to be involved in consciousness. In particular, we find that propofol-induced loss of consciousness is mostly associated with cortico-cortical mechanisms, as opposed to thalamo-cortical ones, and with a substantial decrease in the efficiency of information flow within the network.' If processes related to artificially induced unconsciousness are the same as in naturally induced unconsciousness, then what is the effect on decision-making during recovery from unconsciousness such as awakening?

At some levels of behaviour, we are happy not to consider choice. An aphid (*Acyrthosiphon pisum*) which feeds on legumes has different races which are adapted to different hosts. When a clone adapted to a particular host is moved to a new host, it always performs worse, but over time some clones adapt better than others. This is not the result of choice, but of the small set of genotypes found in each clone.

Haldane (1932, pp. 42–6), in discussing an extensive study of 'criminal behaviour' in identical and fraternal twins, found that 'differences on environment and free-will together' had a significant effect on whether identical co-twins were concordant or discordant in their behaviour, but that fraternal twins were no more likely or unlikely to share the same behaviour as pairs of non-twin siblings. A more recent meta-analysis (Mason and Frick 1994) found that 'antisocial behaviour' indeed has a substantial inherited component in its determination, but that environmental effects were also very important. The conclusion is that, at the population level, and over time, there is no determinism; choice, and in consequence, free will exists.

Turning to more positive behaviour, can love be real in the absence of free will (Boudesseul *et al.* 2016)? 'Falling in love' is a metaphorical description of something happening outside our control, something that must happen, given the two people involved; surely this is determinism? If love is 'simply' biochemical attraction, is it love?

4.5 Conclusions

Overall, what can we say?

There is no real moral imperative to be drawn from evolution by natural selection: a guide to behaviour at the level of common decency can be drawn from the outcomes that we see to be necessary for a society to function well: liberty, equality, sibship support, honesty, co-operation. A standard set of virtues, in fact, but one whose components have all, as discussed above, been shown to have benefits in particular societies of social beings or in species. Living in a way that may be expected to have mutual and reciprocal benefits is then rational, but only in the imaginations of economists do people behave thus.

An understanding of the continuity of life, both as Darwin saw it in the likely monophyletic nature of evolution, and as arises from an understanding of shared inheritance through investigation of DNA and RNA, is available as a basis for respect for our planet and all the life it carries. Indeed, limiting one's use of natural and other resources, apart from one's intelligence and humanity, should always be beneficial. However, these are moral imperatives only to those who feel them; they are not necessary conclusions from what we know.

Natural selection is a simple idea, and the mechanism is close to a tautology, as Lewontin (1969) pointed out. Because it is simple, it is unsatisfactory to many who look at the extraordinary complexity of an ant colony, the human brain or a darts club and who conclude that there must be a complex explanation for its nature. The complex explanations offered to date generally involve something from outside the evidence available in biology. Accordingly, they cannot be the same as the explanation through evolution by natural selection of the existence of the perceived extraordinary complexity; this has involved immense time relative to the time during which we have been investigating it, but is otherwise expected, by Occam's razor, to have been the same set of processes that we see in action today.

A major problem in perception is our difficulty with probability. We exist; our existence has a probability of one. Accordingly, we should scrutinise closely arguments that say we humans, in all our splendour, are highly unlikely to have evolved by natural selection: these arguments are in conflict with the fact of our existence. The hominin fossil record, and the close DNA relationships to extinct lineages such as Neanderthal and Denisovian, not to mention recent DNA changes in our own lineage, such as in lactose metabolism and pigmentation, all show how we are the product of evolution, and the effective agency is natural selection.

What has evolved? In a sense, everything. While it is possible that some particular attribute of an organism has not evolved by natural (including sexual) selection, it has still evolved. Furthermore, as the example of European infanticide (section 1.1) shows, it can also evolve socially.

Altruism has evolved. It is not universal in mammals, but it (or behaviour that can be interpreted as altruism in human terms) is seen in different species. It has been shown to be evolvable.

Co-operation has evolved (section 3.6). Condorcet, Adam Smith and other thinkers of the Enlightenment took its importance in human affairs as being quite as important as co-operation; Darwin went on to consider how it might be advantageous in a biological sense. It has been shown to be evolvable. Its heritability is probably not low (e.g. Cesarini *et al.* 2008).

Virtually every deleterious behaviour trait that has been analysed in humans has indeed sufficient genetical variability to respond to selection, natural or artificial. Natural selection continues, though its pattern is not always recognisable. I have cited the heritabilities in question. In addition, I have mentioned fewer than a dozen specific genes that affect human behaviour, and fewer still than influence animal and plant behaviour. This is out of the thousands of genes that have been identified; the total number of human structural genes, that is genes that code for some particular protein, is fewer than 30,000, and just a catalogue of these genes will require many years of investigation. Interactions among gene products are the norm, so analysis of the pathways involving them, of which I have mentioned fewer than ten, is also in its infancy. To draw inferences regarding ethics therefrom must be hazardous.

Similar to the low number of genes cited is the low number of references to specific aspects of brain function, yet some would say that we cannot begin to comprehend the mind until we know how the brain works, the one comprehending the other. In this context, free will itself may not exist, yet something like free will has evolved; choices are made, and an individual does not necessarily make the same choice each time that very similar circumstances arise. Richard Dawkins's metaphor in *The Selfish Gene* of organisms as 'gigantic lumbering robots' 'manipulating [us] by remote control', 'survival machines' for genes (Dawkins 1976 p. 21) is not necessarily appropriate, never mind correct. He relented in the final sentence of the book 'We, alone on earth, can rebel against the tyranny of the selfish replicators [genes].' (p. 215). He accepts free will, in part, to reach this conclusion. Most biologists do; it is philosophers who find timing tricks in unconscious decision-making important in ruling out free will. Without free will, discussion of human organisms working for and on behalf of their genes is not necessarily appropriate, let alone correct, even if we were to accept that 'genes created us, body and soul' (Dawkins 1976 p. 21)

We can list traits widely regarded as desirable that have evolved: co-operation, discussed above, and parental care, for example. Riddington and Gosler (1995) showed that parental care differs between good and poor environments in the great tit *Parus major* and that it depends on the parental birds' condition. MacColl and Hatchwell (2003) showed that in the long-tailed tit *Aegithalos caudatus* there is significant repeatability in effort between breeding seasons (years): greater than 0.5. Furthermore, the heritability of parental effort in these tits was in the range 0.4 to 0.6. The five-fold range of variation in parental care reported is such that substantial change, of the order of 100%, could be achieved. It is evident from the strong dependence of survival on parental care that parental care is a good in itself, if survival is a good.

Brunetière looked at evolutionary findings in his time and found confirmation for the Fall of Man and the imperfection of man. Thus, he saw biology as providing confirmation for his revelation. We cannot bring a biological ethics from outside biology; we can identify phenomena that might be part of an evolutionary ethics.

We need to consider whence we derive the view that a trait is desirable. Evolved properties of living organisms can be helpful or harmful from an ethical point of view. Co-operation and altruism can be beneficial to a human group, and hence desirable for that group. Family limitation can be beneficial to the species but not to the group. Respect for other living things can be beneficial to the biosphere. Limiting one's use of natural and other resources, apart from one's intelligence and humanity, should always be beneficial to the biosphere. Human threats to the environment have historically been widespread but small in scale. They are now global; warming has occurred on the scale predicted by Arrhenius (1896) and is worsening. An ethics based on respect for the environment and the desire that *Homo sapiens* not become extinct would seem to demand a carbon-neutral economy and a halt to population growth. However, this is not a necessary consequence of understanding extinction by natural selection. Necessity comes from the individual conscience, or not.

Social Darwinism underlies much political thinking today. It is a revelation in the sense that it is a set of lessons drawn from an inspired writer. That this writer, Charles Darwin, would probably not accept the inferences is irrelevant. Huxley (1894c), as pointed out strongly by Daiches Raphael (1958), 'concluded … that the standards of ethics … are *completely* opposed to the principle of natural selection. [In Huxley's words:] "The practice of that which is ethically best – what we call goodness or virtue – involves a course of conduct which, in all respects, is opposed to that which leads to success in the cosmic struggle for existence".' It is in this light that Brunetière was happy to find that the Fall and Original Sin were, as he saw it, supported by then current thinking on evolution by natural selection. There are several difficulties with his happiness.

First, and more obvious, is that concordance between observation and theory is not demonstration that the theory (in this case, the Old Testament) is correct; observation and experimental results can be concordant with an infinity of incorrect theories, but can only contradict and hence disprove or make more precise any particular theory.

Secondly, what we see in the living world fits the theory of evolution by natural selection. Other factors have been and are important. In particular, chance and the laws of physics and chemistry are essential components of evolution. The theory is not static: over the past century, many additions have been made. The role of chance has been thoroughly investigated and, as a result, population size has been shown to be very important. Horizontal gene transfer is steadily assuming extra importance as a major factor: genes have been moved between taxa that are phylogenetically distant, and organelles are being shown to have been, originally, independent micro-organisms. And so on. However, all have been subject to natural selection. 'It may be said that natural selection is daily and hourly scrutinising, throughout the world, every variation, even the slightest; rejecting that which is bad, preserving and adding up all that is good; silently and insensibly working, whenever and wherever opportunity offers, at the improvement of each organic being in relation to its organic and inorganic conditions of life. We see nothing of these slow changes in progress, until the hand of time has marked the long lapse of ages, and then so imperfect is our view into long-past geological ages, that we only see that the forms of life are now different from what they formerly were.' (Darwin, 1859, Ch. 4; he included the word 'metaphorically' before 'be said' in 1860))

As I hope I have made clear, we cannot erect a theory of ethics from natural selection as we now understand it. Brunetière would not have been concerned by this conclusion; his ethics came from revelation, as discussed, like most others'.

Thirdly, because science is always provisional, it is not sensible or safe for it to be used as support for revelation. Revelation, in general, is not provisional; it is absolute. For those to whom revelation is important, provisional support is not support. For others, the (possibly only temporary) support may be of interest, but given that revelation has no intrinsic validity, the support for the 'real' content of the revelation is evidentiary only.

In this context, I should mention a revelation-based view of the origin of the natural world the proponents of which, in notable contrast to Brunetière, regard it as antagonistic to the theory of evolution by natural selection. This is 'intelligent design'. It is not really possible to show that 'intelligent design' is incorrect. Kitcher (2007), for example, explains carefully where its faults lie, but this will not convince those who have taken it up on the basis of faith in something other than science. For example, when it is accepted that the earth is thousands of millions of years old, and hence old enough for evolution by natural selection to have occurred, this simply changes the timescale of 'intelligent design'; it does not disprove 'intelligent design'.

There is here a clear difference from Brunetière: knowing his revelation, he expected to find its confirmation in science, and he did. The proponents of 'intelligent design', however, expect to disprove evolution by natural selection because they consider that it conflicts with their revelation. Their revelation is, of course, based on the same texts as Brunetière's.

De Duve (2009a) presented eight options for the future, on the basis that humanity's current path is disastrous. He has couched them, in essence, as imperatives, not all simultaneously possible. They are all relevant.

First, do nothing. This, he concluded, would probably lead to our extinction, a perfectly natural outcome for any species. It would also, through overpopulation and despoliation of the planet, wreak untold misery on the way to extinction.

Secondly, improve the gene pool. This could be a beneficial outcome, if it led to some of de Duve's other hopes, discussed below. It has the disadvantages already discussed of the widespread view that eugenics is not a good. It may happen through government edict, as has occurred in the past, but it is not clear that our understanding of the genome will lead to improvement, other than by expensive, piecemeal elimination of defective genes.

Thirdly, rewire the brain. It is not clear that the tools are available, even if, as in the case of eugenics, we knew what to do. As I have noted frequently above, general improvement in one trait will have correlated responses, and we do not in general know how, say, a general decrease in envy will influence behaviour in the large.

Fourthly, make an appeal to religion to assist in the task. History does not make one optimistic. De Duve asserts, but does not prove, that an ethics without doctrine is possible; I believe I have shown that such an ethics cannot be based on evolution by natural selection, even if it be accepted that what I have called the belief system of science is not a doctrine. (I think it is.)

Fifthly, protect the environment. From the point of view of the biosphere, if it can be said to have such an attribute, this is an unalloyed good. To the coal-miner or car manufacturer or intensive livestock producer, this may not be the case. It is an imperative from almost any ethical standpoint, but as the history of extinction shows, it is not an evolutionary imperative.

Sixthly, put women in charge. From *Lysistrata* onwards, this has seemed like a good idea.

Finally, check population growth. This is essential for humanity to have a future, but many human agencies, supported by revelation, are against it.

The dog said in 'Silver Blaze' to have done nothing in the night time could not have done nothing, or it would have died; it just did nothing that anyone noticed, which was the 'curious incident' that Sherlock Holmes noticed Doyle, 1892). As a friend remarked to me, 'If a hamster says, 'My brain made me do it,' we can accept the hamster's comment in good faith, but if an adult human says the same thing, we cannot.'

Acknowledgements

I thank C. R. Leach for help with this book and G. R. Fraser and M. G. Mayo for advice on many of the topics over many years.

I am grateful to CSIRO for many years of generous support. Nothing in this book represents or is intended to represent CSIRO policy or practice.

I gratefully acknowledge the generous support of the A. K. A. Abbie Trust.

References

The Morality of Evolutionary Theory
Ferdinand Brunetière

1. One clearly cannot have moral standards without duty or sanction[2];-and this is why nothing could be more useless, or more in error, than to want to build a morality on science in general or from the 'evolutionary theory' in particular. We shall therefore try this in the pages which follow. However, since the scholars themselves do not always reason perfectly, I have decided that it would not be useless to turn against the strongest among them the conclusions of their own science, or, if you will, to try to ruin their

science itself, the pretend philosophy which they try hard today to deduce. 'We read in the holy scripture that the King of Samaria, having wanted to build a stronghold, which would cause fear and trembling in all the towns of the kingdom of Judea, that prince assembled his people and made such an effort against the enemy that he not only ruined their fortress, but used its materials to construct two citadels with which he fortified his frontier...' That is the superb and forthright start of the second sermon of Bossuet *on Providence*; and the orator not being one of those who ornaments his discourse with superfluous comparisons, he continues in

---

[2] One prides oneself, as I know well, on founding such a morality; and I know the book called: *Essai d'un Morale sans obligation ni sanction* [J. M. Guyau, 1885]. In France, we love to play with words! Assuredly, I can say that to live well, one need do nothing but conform with the law and with the dictates of charity, some among us have no need to be 'obliged' to anyone nor to be 'rewarded' [for such a life]. One can at least admit this! There are the sweet natured; and I myself have known lay saints. One can equally conceive that it can become normal, habitual, or if you wish, instinctive, to work to perfect ourselves without a law forcing us to, or it yielding an advantage solely for us , or a future pleasure. There is a great joy in simply understanding many things, and if there are lazy wills, there are others who, rather than rest, would work to fill the gap.

Je suis maître de moi comme de l'univers: – Je le suis, je veux l'être [*Cinna*, Corneille, 1641]

And in a word, nothing is against, in a very distant future, all that we include under the title 'morality' being incorporated into our nature, indeed we could make part of our definition things like spoken language or abstract thought. Man would then be a 'moral' animal as one says, since Aristotle, that he is a 'political' animal; he would do good just as he breathed; he would be virtuous as the tiger is ferocious, or as the sheep is good-natured; and one cannot deny that that would be a beautiful dream; and we recognise the confidence which Mr Guyau, with his usual generosity, holds in the infinite power of *sociology*.

But first of all, when, in place of dreaming, one tries to see such things as they are, it seems that this utopia of a 'morality without duty or sanction' is no less contradictory than all those which we know from our nature and the lessons of history and indeed the conditions of our mortal life. It is not in our nature to 'sacrifice' ourselves; and as has been very well said, 'we do not sacrifice one shovel of coal, when we are cold, to leave to the people of the 20th century the means to drive their locomotives...or their balloons'. On the other hand, if one analyses with a little precision the motives for even the most disinterested of our actions, the pleasure of 'doing the right thing' is surely in itself what we would call a 'sanction'? And after all to conceive of the life of the species as more important or more interesting for each of us than our own well-being, what is this other, from some way in which one takes in order to persuade people, than to pose the principle of 'duty'? Let us thus say nicely, if we wish to understand ourselves, and if the words of the language are not to be put to all sorts of uses, that in good French there is no morality without obligation or sanction than there is religion without the supernatural; that they are not solely connected concepts, but synonyms; and after that, in the same way that one tries to detach religion from the supernatural being who established it, I agree that one tries to base the rules of conduct which depend less on any type of obligation or sanction than on an intelligent disposition of good intentions, but that is no more [derived] from morality than from religion; it is something else and we must call it by another name.

these terms: 'I ponder today, gentlemen, on something similar, and in that peaceful exercise, I choose the example of our armed forces.' Let us follow him in our turn; and, from all the philosophies which authorise science, then *evolutionism* is without doubt 'the most advanced', we shall show that the true interpretation of the doctrine can differ from what many of our scholars say; that there is some means to reduce our knowledge to lessons of eternal morals; and that it does not have finally to be for what would clear it itself in a light which would quite rightly not be 'the flame of science'.

I

2. It is thus that in first place, if we know how to listen, the 'theory of descent [with modification]', – which is like the impregnable fortress, and in any case the master idea of the evolutionary doctrine, – has discredited long ago and ruined, as I hope, the dangerous hypothesis of the 'natural goodness of man'. Naive, or at least as silly as dangerous, has the hypothesis perhaps already inspired the philosophy of the Romans

and the Greeks? It is thus so for those who are dead, and from that!³ But, without going further into this point of learning, it is always that, in the history of modern thought, the 'illusion of the natural goodness of humans' has only dated from the epoch of the Renaissance, and the fortune that it has made from the end of the eighteenth century⁴. It is Diderot who has given the most simple and cynical expression to the thought⁵, in the *Supplément au voyage de Bougainville*, of which I reproduce here only a short but rather elegant passage: 'If you propose to be a tyrant over men, – we read there in neat terms, – civilize yourself; *drive yourself mad from an improvement of a morality contrary to nature*; make it a hindrance to the whole species; hamper its movements with a thousand obstacles; bring to it phantoms that terrify; to make last forever the war in the cave, *and that the natural man must be chained up under the feet of the moral man.*' But, on the contrary, 'you want him happy and free? Don't interfere in his affairs... and remain always convinced that it is not for you, but for them that the wise

---

³ It is remarkable, in this regard, that of all the philosophers of antiquity, it is the Stoics who have taught the most constantly 'that everything which is natural is good'.

⁴ If the movement of the Renaissance had not been, as I believe, in principle and at bottom, other than a 'dechristianization' of European thought, and a return, instinctive at first, then chosen, to the former paganism, it is almost useless here to note that paganism rests totally on the dogma of the divinity of nature, for that is what is the case. But the [good] fortune of the dogma has been twice stopped in its tracks; in the 16ᵗʰ century by the Reformation and in the 17ᵗʰ, by the Counter-reformation and above all by Jansenism. Have I the need, in this context, to remember the force and the eloquence with which Calvin in his *Institution chrétienne* or Pascal in his *Pensées* have spoken of the perversity of our nature? But what is more interesting to note is that the free thinkers …, not completely disengaged, but of the religious belief of Spinoza or Bayle, have not expressed themselves differently from Pascal and Bayle. I say nothing, naturally, of Bossuet or Bourdalone. Molière and la Fontaine, alone or almost alone, would incline to believe that 'nature is good' at least that it would be still better to leave it to itself than to submit to a 'principle of repression'. But Voltaire, – some wish he had, some advantage he wanted to achieve, in his antichristian polemic, – could still not accept the 'goodness of man'; and his conclusion has been that 'we are a kind of monkey which one can train for reason or for folly'. The view of Rousseau would be harder to clarify. It is still the start of *Émile* that one quotes, the well-known sentence: 'Everything is good as it comes from the hands of the Author of Nature…': however, the *Social Contract* is no more than a man who believes in the goodness of nature; and in effect Rousseau believes no more in the concept than he has need of, to base his reasoning thereon. But if someone believes firmly in the proposition, it is Diderot, and with him most of the Encyclopaedists. I propose one day to demonstrate this more fully in speaking of the *Encyclopédie* and the Encyclopaedists.

⁵ It is not I, it is Diderot, who has brought together some part of the two terms 'cynicism' and 'simplicity' as being, in his view, natural neighbours and almost supplementary one to the other.

legislators have kneaded you and made you as you are. *I call on all the political civil and religious institutions ...* Mistrust what he wants to put in order. *To order, that's always to make yourself master of others and to manage them.*[6] And I do not ignore the fact that the *Supplément au voyage de Bougainville* did not appear until 1797, but the ideas that Diderot expressed there are to be found no less in the writings of a Bernardin de St Pierre or of a Condorcet. Danton, Desmoulins, Hébert, Chaumette: they have certainly participated. These ideas have formed the 'sociological' legacy of the 18th century for their heirs. And just as they are at the bottom of our revolutionary laws, it is certain that one finds them as the prime source of our socialist utopias.[7]

3. To tell the truth, I do not believe that anyone dares publicly to sustain these ideas. The excess of the Revolution, the Wars of the Empire, fifty and more years of political agitation have reduced us, since Diderot, to a fairer, or less optimistic, view of humanity. The great Catholic writers of the start of the century, Bonald,

Lamennais – the Lamennais of the *Essay on Indifference,* – Joseph de Maistre have made their contribution (de Maistre above all), of which one too often forgets that he has left us, in his *Evenings in St Petersburg,* the most beautiful image that there could be of the 'struggle for existence'[8] and the most dramatic. Others have followed, Taine, for example; and even Renan, in their *Origins of Contemporary France,* or in *The History of Israel,* to show us the 'natural man' in the truth of his attitude, they have done no more than appropriate the latest results of prehistoric anthropology.[9] But these results have not been made possible other than through 'the theory of descent [with modification]'; and it is good to note that, as we are going to see, it has achieved the ruin of the doctrine of 'the natural virtue of man'.

4. If we do indeed descend from apes, or we share with the apes a common ancestor, and that ancestor in turn comes from something even more 'animal' which is supposed more distant, must it not be that there is some memory, or, as already stated, some 'feeling' of all the forms

---

[6]   *Œuvres complètes de Diderot,* édition Assézat et Maurice Tourneux, t. II, p. 246–247.

[7]   'The social question', it has been said of our time, 'is a moral question'; and one can hear that rather widely. However, in a manner otherwise than intended, the 18th has come to signify precisely the contrary; and if it differs from the 17th, that is without doubt in many other points, but with no advantage in changing 'moral questions' into 'social questions'. Thinking that man is 'naturally good' has finally been found to lead to the explanation of 'social evils' in the vices of institutions, and therefore no remedy is seen or imagined other than to reverse the laws that are believed to have caused the moral misery; if there were no rich, there would be no poor; if there were no priests, there would be no impiety; if there were no 'capitalists', there would be no 'wage-slaves'; if there was no law, there would be no rebels, and in truth I regret that I cannot call to mind the text, but I am sure that it would have taken little to push Diderot to say that there would be no 'criminals' if there were no 'judges'. Moreover, Helvetius (*Discourse* II, Ch. 15) wrote: 'The vices of a people are always hidden *at the bottom of its legislation: it is there that one must search* to tear out its 'productive root'; and that quotation suffices to clarify what I want to say. Insofar as socialism consists in believing that goodwill, or the same virtue of the individual, do not depend on that individual but on the organisation of the State; and as Diderot says again, that 'if the laws be good, the customs will be good', so well expressing the 18th century. One sees the link with the hypothesis of the natural goodness of man. And if it is good to transfer 'the moral questions into social questions', one sees, conversely, what one can say when one says that 'social questions are at bottom nothing other than moral questions'.

[8]   *Evenings in St Petersburg.* 7th conversation.

[9]   If someone should ask me where Renan has expressed his ideas on this point, I would say without delay: 'One must regard primitive humanity as very wicked. What characterised man for centuries, that made ruses, the subtlety with which he acts maliciously, and also that monkey's lust which, without distinction of season, makes the entire year into a perpetual rut.' (*History of Israel,* vol. I, p. 4)

that we have traversed before putting on that form which is ours today? *Vitium hominis natura pectoris*, St Augustine said: 'what is a vice in man is natural in a beast'. Our bad instincts are our inheritance from our first ancestors. But to what title and by what right do we call them 'base', if not because they stop us disengaging from our fundamental animality? Or still more, and always from the 'theory of descent [with modification]', because we have become men insofar as we have already succeeded in surmounting our animality? This is why all those who think that it matters for morality to rest on the idea of the native perversity as its indestructible base have no reason to reject the 'theory of descent [with modification]'; and, to the contrary, they have ten, they have twenty, reasons to permit this. 'The differences in structure between man and the primates that resemble us most' wrote Professor Huxley in the most recent French translation of *Man's Place in Nature*, 'these differences are no greater than those that exist between these last and the other members of the order of primates, of such a nature that, if one has reason to believe that all the primates, man excepted, come from a single primitive stock, there is nothing in the structure of man that authorises us to assign to man a different origin'[10]. This we admit willingly, without hesitation or reserve. Far from us the repugnance of ridiculous vanity! Yes, we have in us, in our blood, and, so to speak, we all have deep in our veins, something of the brutality, the lubricity, the ferocity of the gorilla or the orang-utan! Do we bring with us, besides, nascent seeds of some virtues? That's the question!

And for my part I would rather be tempted to deny it: our 'qualities' alone seem natural to me, health, beauty, vigour, skill; all our 'virtues'[11] seem acquired to me. But what we certainly find within us are the seeds of all our vices, – to start with those which we impute to the iniquity of our social institutions; – and what could there be more natural , I wish to say easier to explain if we are the present term of an infinite series of animal ancestors?

5. So, this is what explains admirably the dogma, – or the myth, as you will, so universal and so profound, – of *original sin*.[12] One does not expect that I enter here into the examination of the controversies which he has raised, and which are moreover as much outside my competence as outside my subject. But, if we strip the dogma of its theological wrappings, and we incline ourselves no more than a little in the Protestant direction, which is also Jansenist, to what have we reduced it? Not to mix ourselves in it, we can leave it to Calvin to speak. 'Original sin is a corruption and hereditary perversity of our nature, which being expanded into all parts of the soul, makes us guilty first of the wrath of God, *then afterwards produces in us the deeds that the Scriptures call deeds of the flesh* ... By which, those who have defined original sin to be a flaw in original justice ... how much that in those words they would have included all the substance, however, they have not sufficiently expressed the force of this one. *Because, our nature is not only empty and destitute of all good, but it is so fertile in every kind of evil, that it could not be idle.*'[13] A true evolutionist, a convinced evolutionist could certainly

---

[10]   T. H. Huxley, *La Place de l'homme dans la nature*, new edition; Paris, 1891, J.-B. Baillière, p. 1.

[11]   'And you, plagues of God, who knows if genius is not one of your *virtues*,' said Lamartine in his *Bonaparte*; and Renan, hardier, has asked if 'beauty' could not be a virtue? Evidently I do not here take the word 'virtue' in that sense; and still less in the sense of the Renaissance Italians when they praised, with an admiration mixed with fear, the 'virtue' of a Sforza or a Malatesta. Or, in other words, I do not separate the notion of 'virtue' from the notion of 'good morality' known or presented as such; and some difference which there could be between individuals, even of a species of animal, that is from the 'innateness' of this kind of virtue that I can hardly believe in.

[12]   Lamennais, in the second volume of his *Essay on Indifference*, has tried to regain the universality of the dogma of the fall of man in the traditions of antiquity.

[13]   *Institution chrétienne*, texte française, Édition Baum, Cunitz et Reuss, 1859, Brunswick, vol. I, p. 293.

not express himself in terms more precise or explicit. Shall I dare yet to suggest that there could be something still better? And why not, if I believe it? The 'theory of descent [with modification]' has just given, after a fashion, a physiological basis for the doctrine of original sin; and the principal difficulty which still prevents the agreement of both disbelievers and even some believers is one that Darwin and Haeckel themselves have raised.

6. Because the dogma shocks reason. It contradicts the idea that is commonly adopted of the power of freedom. But it shocks above all our ideas of justice; and what seems 'monstrous' to strongly honest people, it that it is we who are punished, from birth, for a crime or a fault which we have not been able to prevent from commission. *Quod admoneri non potest ut caveatur, imputari non potest ut puniatur!* [Something like: What one can't be advised to avoid, one can't be blamed for in order to be punished.] However, in place of softening a hard doctrine, one renders it harder still, and what is only difficult to understand, it seems that a kind of after-pleasure has been taken to make it inconceivable to us. 'What an astonishing thing! – wrote Pascal in a celebrated passage in his *Pensées*, – that the mystery most distanced from our knowledge, which is that of the transmission of sins, must be something without which we cannot have any knowledge of ourselves! Because there is nothing that shocks our reason more than to say that the sin of the first man has rendered guilty those who, being most distant from that source, are incapable of participating in it. And yet, without that mystery, *the most incomprehensible of all*, we are incomprehensible to ourselves. The knot of our condition takes its folds and its turns in that abyss, so that man more inconceivable without this mystery than this mystery is incomprehensible

to man!' Voltaire triumphed on these last words, and cried out in turn: 'What a strange explanation! Man is inconceivable without an inconceivable mystery!…' In which, moreover, he paid no more attention than that, every day, we 'explain' thus things that we hardly understand by things that we understand not at all: gravitation by *attraction*; the combination of elements by *chemical affinity*; the phenomena of life by *the properties of organised matter*. But he was not completely wrong, in the sense that he reasoned in a manner absolutely 'analogous' to the philosophy of his time. The science of our time has in part cleared up the mystery. It sufficed for him to transpose it from the theological or metaphysical framework to the physiological. And what Pascal called 'inconceivable' or 'incomprehensible' the theory of descent has used to establish the acceptability, the probability, the near-certainty on the same basis of natural history.[14]

7. What moreover the orthodox exegesis, – I mean Protestant or Catholic, – cannot accept in this interpretation of dogma, that is what we are for the moment precisely to investigate. We here do no more than indicate a 'possibility' of an agreement between dogma and science. Abbott de Broglie wrote two or three years ago: 'Neither the successive appearance of [different] forms nor their linkage are opposed to the teachings of the Church. What is more, transformation itself, in the form provided by Darwin, may be mentioned in Catholic schools.'[15] And long before de Broglie, – in a well-known essay on *The limits of natural selection*, – the naturalist [Alfred] Russel Wallace declared expressly that the forces that could bring about the transformation of species were incapable of explaining the passage from animal to man. He repeated this in 1889, in his book on *Darwinism*.[16] But as that hardly stops the widespread support for

---

[14]   On the subject of original sin, see: – Bossuet, *Élévations sur les mystères*, 7th week, in particular the 5th and 7th 'rises'; and – Lamennais, *Essay on Indifference*, vol. III, Ch. 27.

[15]   Abbott de Broglie: *Past and Present of Catholicism in France*, 1 vol.-18; Paris, 1892, Plon, p. 113.

[16]   Alfred Russel Wallace, *Natural selection*, (translated into French by Alphonse de Candolle, 1 vol. in 8°; Paris, 1872, Reinwald, p. 348–391. See particularly p. 403: 'If Mr Darwin is not anti-Darwinist when he admits that animals and

'the theory of descent [with modification]', and even its strengthening or development by new arguments, it is all that we need remember here. For contemporary science, the abyss where 'the knot of our condition, in to the words of Pascal, takes its folds and turns', is the complexity of our family tree. Or, on yet other terms, a dogma which has no value or significance other than believing it, and has taken it for the free-thinker, courtesy of the 'theory of descent [with modification]'; and finally it is that, from a 'symbol' which was repugnant to our fathers, evolutionism, in our times has made almost a reality.

8. Shall I mention now the consequences which follow? I recommend them to the attention of the strange moralists who, from everything that they retain of the evolutionary doctrine, require that we favour ourselves what they call, with emphasis, 'the development of all our powers', and 'the expansion of all our potential"![17] But to the contrary, and in conformity with the 'theory of descent [with modification]'; if we have not become men; if our species is not differentiated from those; and in two words, if the 'human sovereignty' is not realised into a position to disengage from, and to an extent has disengaged from, the ancient animality, 'human sovereignty' does not exist, cannot persist, cannot last; and we ourselves live only at the price of combat which we must make daily against the humiliating fate of our first beginnings. What we have to in any case, and indeed first of all, it to tame, to submit, and to dominate what we find in our instincts that brings us close to animals. Because 'What is *natural*, that is no more than the law of the strongest or most skilled which is sovereign in the animal world, but precisely what is not

human; – what is *natural,* that is what the jackal or the hyena, the eagle or the vulture, when they are pressed by hunger, [do], obedient to the drive of their ferocity, but precisely that is not *human*; – what is *natural* is what the 'king of the desert' or the 'sultan of the jungle' [does] in strolling from female to female and fight the object of their choice in the childhood of their race, but precisely that is not *human*; – and what is *natural* is that each generation among the animals, unfamiliar with what has preceded it in life, must be the same as that which follows it, now that is not *human*.'[18] Please pardon me if I quote myself thus, if what I said six or seven years ago I can say not better today. It is the 'theory of descent [with modification]' which obliges us in everything from birth to remember our origins so as not to be unfaithful to them! Ah! Who does not indeed see that to develop all our 'powers' and all our 'potentialities', if we miss some more elevated obligation, at the very least we betray the interests of the entire species? We would be working to damage it, in recommitting it to the imperfection of its own past. We would retreat rather than advance; and all that we acquire in new power over nature would not be counterbalanced by new power over ourselves; we would strengthen ourselves insensibly in a barbarism more hideous than previously, for our still brutal instincts would be served from now on by more powerful means.

9. On the same basis of 'descent from animals', about which there is without doubt nothing mystical, – it seems only that we can establish the true foundation of education. 'Let do and let pass!' [i.e. do not interfere, François Quesnay] I do not know today what the value of that maxim may be in political economy; and

---

plants perhaps do not have a common ancestor…I am no longer myself when I make myself see that in man certain phenomena cannot be completely explained by natural selection, *and seem to indicate at the same time some higher law.*' And indeed compare the 15th chapter of *Darwinism*, by Wallace, translated by H. de Varignay; Paris, 1891, Lecrosnier et Babé. This book forms part of the *Bibliothèque d'évolutioniste.*

[17] It is again from Mr Guyau that I borrow these terms, and in truth, I am sorry that I have to contradict him so often! However, I would be able so to do if his main aim had not been other than to 'laicise' morality and religion; if anyone other than he had been able so to succeed; and as for me, is it not precisely against this 'laicisation' that I protest?

[18] See in my *Critical Essays*, the chapter called *Question of morality.*

I fear furthermore that in attacking it one generally interprets it wrongly! Indeed, it is from the time and relates to the time when the grand task of economists was to combat restrictive legislation on the grain trade. But the essential problem of education is not just that of determining with sufficient exactitude what one can humanely 'neither let do nor let pass'. And what is it that one can neither 'let do nor let pass'? If you consider it closely enough, it is still, it is always, what would tend, in encouraging the dominance of animal motives over social, to take us back to our original state.[19] Education has the object of helping us to overcome our instincts and thus to realise the definition of our species. Before being human and in order to become human, we must use education to clear us of vice and the dirt of our far distant origins. But if we start today to understand more clearly, and above all in a manner more conscious than ever, is it not true that the merit or the honour comes in large part from the 'theory of descent [with modification]'?

10. And the same theory can even serve to make us better understand the grandeur and the beauty, one might almost say the 'sanctity', of the social institution. Because, on one side, for us to escape from the tyranny of our animal impulses, it is not too much, it is hardly sufficient for all of us, all the forces of society working together, to combat nature. But, on another side, if we agree that we descend from animals, then neither the true interests of the individual would differ in principle from those of the species, nor those of the species run contrary to those of the individual. They seem sometimes to oppose each other; and a certain philosophy seems to have taken on the task of exaggerating the opposition and exacerbating the conflict. 'Fish,' it has been said, 'are required by their nature to swim, and the big ones are required to eat the small ones. That is why water *belongs* to fish, and the large eat the small *by natural right*. It follows that each being has a sovereign right over all that it can ... And we admit in this regard no difference between men and other beings.'[20]

11. But this argument of Spinoza, like all arguments of the same genre, has no more than the appearance of logic and of truth to be found in the hypothesis of the absolute fixity of species. Species vary? And in varying they sometimes perfect themselves? The reasoning in this case is no less arbitrary and destructive than it is cynical. Organised society can have no other object than to tend towards the perfection of the species, and the individual has no other than to aim towards the perfection of society. Intellectual or physical, every degradation of the individual, – not simple every degradation, but even his obstinacy in persisting in his present state, such as it is, without the least wish to correct himself, – will slow down, will retard, will delay, when it does not halt, the evolution of society. On another side, if some other catastrophe interrupts and paralyses social evolution, it is in his own development than the individual will find himself blocked. The 'theory of descent [with modification]', in reducing to the same principle, which is the triumph of animality, the 'individual duty' and the 'social duty', has certainly not put an end to the eternal between community and individual. But is it not something that it has stopped us from seeing here a 'law of nature'?[21] and on the contrary that it has identified the conditions of individual progress with

---

[19] Here I just want to give an indication of the problem, having discussed it in my *Education and Instruction*.

[20] Spinoza, *Tractatus theologico-politicus*, ch. 16, *Pisces a Natura determinati sunt ad natandum, magni ad minores comedendum; adeoque pisces summo naturali jure aqua potiuntur, et magni minores comedunt.*

[21] Yes, it is certainly 'something'! And indeed something more significant than one would first believe, if it is true that at all times so-called 'laws of nature' have constituted, by virtue of their obscurity itself, the principal obstacle to progress. We would willingly say that what Moliere said in his *Criticism of the school for women*: 'It seems to us to hear speak that the rules of the art would be the greatest mysteries in the world; however, they are not those easy observations that good sense has made'; and which last up until the same good sense that has made them destroys them. Has not slavery

those of societal progress, in identifying them with the consequent law of the existence of a 'human kingdom'?

II

12. It follows from what I have shown that the only form of 'progress' which truly merits the name is 'moral progress'. We bring forward some examples. One reads in a recent book, on *The origin of marriage in the human species*[22]: 'The history of marriage ... is the history of a relationship in which *women have gradually defeated the passions, the prejudices and the egoistical interests of men.*' There is the picture of true progress! There is another, and of the same order, I can say, example of moral progress, to have in our time – and speaking of a certain school – favoured the dividing up of land in inheritance. 'A family' – Michelet has written somewhere – 'which from being hired workers has become a property owner acquires self-respect, raises itself in its own estimation, and is thereby changed; *it reaps the harvest of virtue!* The sobriety of the father, the saving ways of the mother, the courageous work of the son, the chastity of the daughter, are these fruits of liberty, are these good materials, I beg of you, are they treasures for which one can pay too dearly?'[23] I agree with Michelet! And, under a barbarous name, it is progress when we try, as we all do today, to substitute *altruism* for the principle of individualism which we have made for too long – and too inhumanely – the goal of our activities, the law of political economy, and the condition of happiness.[24] Yes! There is true progress! And how much in the sense that

---

in its time passed for a 'law of nature'? We challenge these grand words that some scholars abuse, and which express all too often that an end to non-examination that they oppose to ideas of which they dread the consequences.

[22] Édouard Westermarck, *The origin of marriage in the human species*, translated by H. de Varignay; Paris, 1895, Guillaumin, p. 518.

What makes this book particularly interesting most instructive is its complete disagreement with what Darwin, Spencer, Bachofen, Morgan, Tylor and so many others have taught on the topic, and which has passed for so long as 'scientific' truth. On learns from Westermarck among other things 'that marriage, generally speaking, has become more lasting, the more humanity has progressed': which tends, to speak like the anthropologists, to make, in the increasing easiness of divorce which our laws make, a *processus* of going backwards.

See particularly on this question of the rights of women the very fine work of Paul Gide: *Study on the deprived conditions of women*, 1867, and new edition, 1885.

[23] Michelet, *The people*. 'In that abject land, he has also said, magnificently, the peasant only sees the gleanings of the gold of liberty.'

[24] If I am asked what I mean by 'moral progress'; by what signs I believe it can be recognised; and if indeed it has some relationship to 'intellectual progress' or 'scientific progress'?

The response is not easy; and, for example, if I propose that 'moral progress' consists in progress growing from the spirit of solidarity; I can be answered that in that case the invention and application of electricity and of steam power have thus been singularly favourable for it. I really don't know; it is not a case that I can examine; and I limit myself to admitting that it is indeed as much moral progress as it is progress in the spirit of solidarity, but that would be neither the measure nor the definition. On another side, to make it consist in 'the expansion of all our powers and all our capabilities' would seem to make it the part too fine of 'individualism'. In what then shall we say that it consists? And where shall we put it? Because, one feels, one is sure, we have had twenty times the cruel experience that 'moral progress' is not 'intellectual progress', since the most knowledgeable is not the most virtuous; and assuredly, if progress in natural history or in organic chemistry has favoured something, that something is not progress in 'sanctity'.

Provisionally, I propose to define 'moral progress' as the advance each of can make in self-detachment and self-denial; while expecting others to improve this definition, I have to note that it has three advantages: – it is distinct from 'scientific progress' and 'intellectual progress'; – there is no implication of utility to human society; – and lastly it conforms to the idea all morality and every religion are formed from virtue.

we still have to achieve or pursue it! But, just as after all the destructive power of dynamite must be much greater than that of black powder, or a cannon, what was taken care of by the mouth in the past is today by the yoke, do you see there in truth on which we can make ourselves so proud? Are you really sure that we should so much admire chemistry, which has, in increasing [the supply of] alcohols, multiplied the causes of degeneracy, of decay, of extinction of the race? And in increasing the 'average life expectancy', do we flatter ourselves by chance into thinking that we shall never die?[25] This is what I would wish on no one! And what is more, frankly, no one would wish it. Schopenhauer said of the thought of death that it was 'the leader of the Muses of philosophy'; and one can say nothing truer, albeit less pretentiously. We would not think that solely, if we were not dying, and if we did not know that we must

die! But, what's more, the thought of death is very condition for morality, if all 'immorality' does other than proceed from our too animal love of life![26]

13. Since it is always this kind of material progress that is boasted of, – and by the way there is no speaking more in the sense or in the imagination, – a happy novelty of the evolutionary doctrine will thus be to have established solidly what was nothing but relative, essentially precarious and intermittent. Contemporaneous with and connected to the theory of the natural goodness of man, the theory of 'infinite perfectibility'[27] must disappear with it; and if 'authority' could suffice to decide the question, I would only have to choose among savants and philosophers. Is it not Claude Bernard who defined evolution as 'a march in a direction whose end has been fixed in advance'?[28] And read again, in the *First principles* of Herbert Spencer, the

---

[25] In this regard, see the hopes with which Descartes, *Discourse on Method*, part 6; and Condorcet, *Sketch of the history of the progress of the human mind*, 10th Age, have lulled their readers. Ah! They were hardly 'pessimists'! And one does not know what one should most admire, their naivety or their hopes, or the fear of death of which this is the ugly witness.

[26] This would be easy to demonstrate, if Bourdalone had not done it, long ago, in one of his best sermons: *On the thought of death*; and after him, less theologically, in one of the most curious appendices of his great work Schopenhauer, whom no one could suspect of being a 'Jesuit'.

[27] I have spoken earlier about the great mistake of the 18th century being the belief in 'the goodwill of nature' and I do not retract anything! But the error has not become less, and I shall say willingly, if the consequences have not been less grave, that the crime is no less great in having believed in the 'infinite perfectibility' of man and society.

One searches far and wide for the origin of this idea of *Progress*, and, as happens when one really knows how to look, one finds it everywhere. But in fact, like the idea of the 'goodwill of nature', it is contemporaneous with the Renaissance; and Bacon and Descartes would doubtless have concurred; but its composition, if I can so phrase it, and its philosophical fortune only date from the end of the 17th century. I have tried to show this several times. *Parallels between Ancients and Moderns* by Charles Perrault seems to me the first work one can conceive the whole extended future and even indicate some of the applications. Fontenelle, and after Fontenelle Voltaire, and after Voltaire, the encyclopaedists have developed Perrault's hints. Turgot gave them the rights to the city at the Sorbonne. And finally Condorcet in his *Sketch of the history of the progress of the human mind* has developed the intangible dogma of which Saint-Simon, Auguste Comte and Pierre Leroux have been the apostles in our time.

[28] Claude Bernard, *Lessons on the phenomena of life common to plants and animals*. Vol. I, page 33.

We have to note in this connexion that Bernard did not wish thereby to define the evolution of living beings, that is to say those of which the literal nature is to be by definition to be condemned to die; and Bernard was without doubt correct! But whence comes the right to believe that humanity could be eternal? And to the contrary, since life has certainly 'begun' on the earth, who can doubt that it will one day 'end'?

let us be certain that the 'end is fixed before the start'; and that at each hour of our existence we come closer to death, so all progress of the species forwards it towards annihilation.

chapter entitled *The instability of homogeneity*! To which, if one adds, as one must, that this march has, moreover, times of cessation or even reversal, this is then what one will see that rather than being suitable, or just analogous, for the idea of progress, the idea of evolution would be above all the opposite. Material progress buys, indeed it can afford; its conquests have never been certain, stable, definitive; and, when we are the most inflated is the moment when *force majeure* demonstrates harshly our vanity.

14. Recently, when I asked how much, for what part, the development of industry by science, had contributed in our times to the increase in the weight of human inequality, I received as answer no more than evasions or pleasantries which gave hardly more honour to humanity than to the mind of their authors. But he saw more clearly, someone who called himself Cardinal Pecci, when he wrote in a *Pastoral letter* of 1877: 'In the presence of those workers worn out before their time by the fact of a heartless greed, we ask ourselves if the followers of this godless civilisation, *in lieu of achieving progress*, did not reject us several centuries back.' And the economists themselves agree, -some economists, at least, Mr Fawcett in England, Mr de Laveleye in Belgium, or above all in France itself[29]: 'It is incontestable that capital accumulates in our industrial societies by reason of their progress. As the improved processes of modern production produce more and more by mechanisation... it follows that the sum of the profits received by the upper class grows rapidly. 'But he continues, a little naively: 'However, it is not certain that the conditions of the workers have worsened!' No, doubtless! This is not certain, if the workers themselves are no more than machines! But if they are human like us, if they have senses and feelings like us, their conditions have 'worsened' with all the bitterness of the comparisons that they cannot fail to make. Sourness, envy, let us put moreover what would there be 'bad feelings', and fight or try to calm them in their hearts! Preach resignation and solidarity to them. What more? Let us see, if we can, how much the peasant of the 17th century, the peasant of La Bruyère, was unhappier than the miner of Carmaux or the steersman of our transatlantic ships; we shall make no more of what the 'facts' might be than they are! The advances of industry, which are the advances of science, have brought about, in their turn, they have created entirely new forms of 'misery' in the world, sharper, more intolerable; and to count on later advances in science and industry to remedy them, I don't know if that is perhaps political homoeopathy, but I do say that it is a chimaera, and I say this in the name of science, since I say it in the name of the evolutionary doctrine.[30] No progress without compensation, this is what we learn, effectively and, – well

---

[29]   Émile de Laveleye: *Contemporary Socialism*, p. xlii, xliii.

[30]   From whom come these words?

'Whoever knows the life of the population in all the large industrial centres of our country or of other countries knows that misery rules over *an ever-increasing mass* of this population. I do not pretend to the title of philosopher and I have a horror of all sentimental rhetoric. I simply try, as a naturalist, to understand the facts which come to my attention, and to ponder over enough of the information to draw the obvious conclusions. And I believe that the following statement is only the expression of a sad truth: in industrial Europe there is not a manufacturing town which does not contain a living population as I have just said, and a population more numerous still, living on the edge of a social abyss into which they are thrown by the least cessation of work. For each increase in population, *a part of the mass falls into the ditch*, and the number of unfortunates destined so to fall grows daily.' Huxley himself said just five or six years ago: What would it serve the human Prometheus to have stolen fire from heaven, if he must be its servant? To have subjugated the spirits of heaven and earth, if the vulture of poverty continues to gnaw into living flesh? And to keep him on the border of destruction?'

But the author of the book from which I took these quotations from one of the last *Lay Sermons*, the great English naturalist, Mr Benjamin Kidd, in his *Social Evolution*, goes much further still; trying to go back to the source of the evil to find the remedy, he suggests no more than a return to the idea of religion.

before Darwin or Haeckel had appeared, – this was one of the best established laws of what call philosophical anatomy. 'Any organ, whether normal or pathological,' wrote Geoffroy Saint-Hilaire in 1818, 'never acquires an extraordinary prosperity without another part of the systems or its relationships suffering to an equivalent extent.'[31] This is what Goethe has expressed in a livelier manner: 'The chapters of the budget which must regulate the expenditure of nature are fixed in advance; – if nature wishes to dispense advantage on one side, she hardly meets an obstacle, but she is forced to restrain herself elsewhere.'[32] And finally Darwin himself, more practically, as befits his nationality: 'It is difficult to make a cow produce a lot of milk and to fatten her at the same time… The same varieties of cabbage do not produce both an abundance of foliage and of oily seeds… As the seeds contained in our fruits tend to atrophy, the fruit itself gains greatly in size and quality.'[33] And the law is so simple; it verifies itself so constantly in nature; it so conforms to the lessons of history and of daily life that, if it astonishes the reader, it must be because its explicit expression awaited the 19th century and Geoffroy Saint-Hilaire.

15. Is this to deny progress? I would say above that it is on the contrary to affirm it, it is to demonstrate it, – as much as 'travel', as 'change', as 'movement', – but moreover it is to modify the idea profoundly. There are false movements, and history is full of disastrous changes, those that have only been accomplished to the detriment of something or someone.

I know that the fruit falls in the wind which shakes it, that the bird loses its feather and the flower its scent; that creation is a great wheel which cannot move on without crushing someone;

[Translation of Victor Hugo in *The Penguin Book of French Poetry: 1820–1950*

Je sais que le fruit tombe au vent qui le secoue Que l'oiseau perd sa plume et la fleur son parfum *Je sais que notre monde n'est qu'une grande roue Qu'il ne peut se mouvoir sans écraser quelqu'un*]

16. It is in 'society' as it is in 'nature'. Some progress compensates for itself or, in some sense, annuls itself; but others pay more than they are worth; and in a factor of material progress, I hardly know that they would be for the species a growth of happiness or of dignity. 'In a century,' it has been said, and perhaps it was not a scholar but an anthropologist who said it, 'Western Europe has produced more inventions than the whole of mankind did in twenty centuries. But the immensity of the material results must have been compensated for by an equal sum of anguish and distress resulting from the struggle of man against man. The result is hardly visible, tears and sweat can hardly be weighed, despair cannot be gauged, and the memory of a suicide is soon lost. But who does not see that the two kinds of struggle being engendered by the same love of money, *the power of their benefits in the material domain measures exactly the magnitude of their disasters in the human domain*'?[34] A good time to

---

31 *Life, Works and Scientific Teaching of Étienne Geoffroy Saint-Hilaire*, by his son Isidore Geoffroy Saint-Hilaire; Paris, 1847, P. 214, 215.

32 *Scientific Works of Goethe* [in French], analysed by Mr Ernest Faivre, p. 130.

33 Darwin *The Origin of Species*, French edition 1876, p. 159. See also *Variation in animals and plants* ch. 21 on selection *by man*; and ch. 25 on *Correlated variability.*

34 *Depopulation and Civilisation*, by Arsène Dumont, p. 243; Paris, 1890, Lecrosnier and Babé.
    We recall in the past having noted this volume, of which we a far from approving all the conclusions, but which we must not recognise the less as being one of the most remarkable volumes in the *Bibliothèque anthropologique*. It contains, at first glance, no more than a 'theory of the birth rate', but the birth-rate itself depends on so many causes, through which, just by enumerating and analysing them, Mr Dumont has had to touch on the most serious questions that 'sociology'

talk! But there is what one forgets when one fills one's mouth with the grand word 'progress'. Because, of what does it consist, I ask you, oh… scholars that you are, this 'progress' that you boast about, if ever these workers' claims have received nothing and yet appeared justified? If the 'psychological misery' and the 'moral distress' seem to grow every day? And in the whole of Europe, over the last fifty or sixty years, the number of suicides has more than tripled? In the Congo, there is hardly a suicide; there are without doubt no religions that advise their faithful to clear up their life by a voluntary death! Alas! One single thing is certain, which is that we go on trying or, as one says colloquially, we make a gesture; but one thing is dubious, problematic and worrying, which is to know if we are making progress; – this, here again it is the theory of evolution which warns us.[35]

17. If the word evolution, as one has the air too often of believing, were effectively synonymous with progress – or, in other words, if these were always and constantly the best endowed, the nearest neighbours to the ideal perfection of their kind, who come out victorious from the struggle for existence, – one could not explain the stubborn survival of inferior types; and their defeat would have to finish by their annihilation. Yes they continue to live, and their fecundity does not seem to diminish, – scientific research seems to indicate rather the contrary, – we do not seem to catch a glimpse of 'progress' which could triumph over their persistence. Among men as in nature, will always be inferior types, and, to say again something more, in the future as in the past, it is their inferiority itself which will be their guarantee of eternity. 'The best endowed' are not always 'the fittest'; that depends on the conditions of the struggle; and it can be, it can happen every day that a deficiency, a defect or a malformation itself can be turned to advantage.[36]

18. The evolutionists willingly quote: 'Have we not seen what happened when the grey rat was introduced into Europe, and there was a struggle with the indigenous rat and the mouse? From those two species a single one survived before the grey rat's invasion. Is it the black rat or the mouse, the one bigger, armed with stronger teeth, the other smaller and weaker? It

---

raises; and further, what is so rare in such writings, his book is truly a work of good faith. Is this perhaps why the work has passed unnoticed?

[35] It will be necessary that these ideas finish by making their way in the world, or rather that they are going to do so, and I find the proof in the following lines: 'So do not believe too much in the force, in the organisation, *in the science…* these are the weapons which can fall into the hands of the spirit of destruction, and *one could see the spectacle of applied science reducing all to barbarism.* I believe indeed that we shall avoid the catastrophe… what if progress, leaving a little aside its inventions and its mechanics, is applied to the moral being.' This I read very recently, dated 3 September, and where, do you believe? In the *Écho de Paris.*

[36] This suffices to 'make a fool of' the proposition which one still sometimes sees issue from the pens of certain physiologists who, from the doctrine of evolution in general, and from the theory of natural selection in particular, all that they have understood, this is what they should be, by virtue of their science, the counsellors, the guides and the masters of civil life. We owe to them already the superstition of *athletics*, which would tend to nothing less, if we were listening, than to reintegrate into our civilised societies the brutal empire of physical strength; and here again they ask that we deal with the means to prohibit the marriage of all those amongst us of whom the 'performance' does not promise beautiful 'products'. And without doubt they are the ones who would judge conjugal ability! And when a marriage did not succeed, they would untie the knot! They would also demand that defective or puny babies be exposed or destroyed. And you will see that they will arrive one day. But, meanwhile, and from all the 'mysteries' of science of which those of reproduction would not be the most mysterious, they forget that, in the true spirit of the evolutionary doctrine, there could be no modification [mutation] which could not be the starting point of a useful variation. This is the secret of nature! They forget also, as we do when we work far from the observations, that this is today a problem more obscure than finding out to what extent 'acquired characters' are inherited.

is the mouse. Precisely on account of its weakness, or, to speak more precisely, on account of its small size, which allowed it to find asylum in the narrow holes where its enemy could not destroy it.'[37] But another, more human, example gives even more food for thought: it is that of the Chinese of New York or San Francisco; 'more dangerous for socialism, – and for the American worker, I imagine, – than the most ferocious capitalists, working, as they do, for nothing and of an equal work capacity, never put off, never tired, fifteen or sixteen hours at a stretch. With them, labour is debased, and they must always be protected against the fury of their white competitors whom they ruin in a few years, if one leaves them free to work.'[38] There are always these Chinese among us, who will be strongly against us from their inferiority itself, and by whom 'material progress' becomes sooner or later the worst enemy of intellectual and moral progress. The least worried, the least concerned about those things that alone bring about human dignity, all those who are just greedy to play, the least 'well endowed', in a word, become the 'best adapted'; and just as they have already triumphed in metaphysics, they end by winning in all those applications of physics or physiology which do not have immediate application, industrial or commercial.[39]

19. Rather listen to them celebrate science! The telegraph, the telephone, dyes, 'refrigerated goods wagons', the vile factories that dismember sheep and pigs by the hundreds of thousands, there you have what they admire! Have they ever heard of Ampère or of Cauchy? But they all know 'the inventor' Edison. What is Pasteur for them? A great chemist, an illustrious physiologist, the renewer of biology? No, just the conqueror of rabies and diphtheria. They know Liebig, too, for his beef extract! And they do not see that in assessing science thus, they reduce it at once to the level of the worst popularism. Their enthusiasm is drawn from the way that science satisfies their coarse appetites! Much less they doubt that their hands work to dry up the source of their future 'progress', if they cannot derive such from the heights of metaphysics or abstract pondering.[40] The Chinese are perhaps an example, of whom the civilisation was perhaps halted by having no ideal other than well-being. And for all these reasons, who will say that in the end what one calls so easily 'progress' would not sometimes be a kind of decline?

20. This is in any case the question that the evolutionary doctrine authorises us to put. And during that short time that we have known ourselves, that we can recall as our history, – just three or four thousand years, – how many civilisations have not disappeared? I want to say, how many denials by experience have been inflicted on the theory of continuous progress?

> Egypt, like a sad mother, who, in her pride, hides her beaten child under her coat, seated beside the Nile, wrapped, sinking, in her dress of sand, her flat-nosed giants kicked in the face by the brutal foot of Cambyses

> [Victor Hugo *Comme une mère sombre, et qui, dans sa fierté, Cache sous son manteau son enfant souffleté, L'Egypte*

---

[37] Mathias Duval: *le Darwinisme*, p. 521; Paris, 1886, Lecrosnier et Babé.

[38] Paul Bourget, *Outre-Mer* [Overseas].

[39] It seems indeed that the effects are already to be seen, if, in every country, the mediocrity of the deliberative assemblies [parliaments] is not the likeness with universal suffrage which names them.

[40] One reads in Plutarch's *Life of Marcellus*: 'Archimedes has had a heart so high and an understanding so deep that he never deigned to leave in writing any work on how to erect all those machines of war for which he acquired fame and renown: he worked not for human science but much sooner for divine wisdom. So famed for all this science of the invention and construction of machines, and generally for all the skill which brought some utility to setting them to work, in vile, base and mercenary ways, he employed his mind and his studies to write solely things of which the beauty and subtlety had no link to necessity.'

au bord du Nil assise Dans sa robe de sable enfonce enveloppés Ses colosses camards à la face frappes Par le pied brutal de Cambyse.]

21. What the invasion and brutal conquest have done to ancient Egypt, or Carthage, or Rome itself; what these could do to us tomorrow, to our arts and science, other means could effect it, which would act no less surely; and according to a profound spectator, 'if there are peoples who let the light be torn from their hands, there are others who extinguish it themselves under their feet.'[41]

22. This is what has happened – for reasons I only sketch today – to the Greeks, for example, or the Italians of the Renaissance, the most intelligent, the most gifted and also, in every sense of the word, the most 'advanced' of the peoples of their times. Their civilisation has perished under the excess of their own principle. They have died from believing that art could exercise on their life a domination as absolute, unique and illimitable as science today claims to arrogate to itself. It thus committed 'beautiful' crimes, 'aesthetic' crimes, and it commits today 'scientific' or 'scholarly' crimes! But if one said that the achievements of these lost civilisations are not themselves lost; if one added that other civilisations have followed or replaced them, or have surpassed them; if one repeats once more that 'nothing can be created, nothing lost [only transformed: Lavoisier]', one hardly cares that a particular civilisation has perished, since humanity continues to progress, I respond with another question[42]; I add in my turn that it is extremely difficult to resolve; and I say that it is still more so here when the evolutionary doctrine is involved. There are 'regressions' in history, there is 'decadence', as in nature; and to get away from the chimaera of 'infinite progress' we need do no more than invoke the conclusions of science itself.

23. 'It appears to us to be one of the many peculiar merits of [Mr Darwin's] hypothesis', wrote Professor Huxley many years ago, '*that it involves no belief in a necessary and continual progress of organisms.*' And elsewhere: 'Suppose, for example, a return of the glacial epoch and a spread of polar climatal conditions over the whole globe. *The operation of natural selection under these circumstances would tend, on the whole, to the weeding out of the higher organisms and the cherishing of the lower forms of life.*'[43] This supposition seems too arbitrary, perhaps? Then here, on regression, are the

---

[41] A. de Tocqueville, *Democracy in America* (in French), III, part 1, Ch. 10.

[42] Indeed, there are so-called 'truths' or 'commonplaces' which are only true in general, or better still, to an extent one decides to hold them true, but they do not survive examination. What is moreover most comical or saddest is that the most determined partisans of the doctrine of 'continuous progress' are the same as those who consider the rise of Christianity as a veritable 'regression', who have said this in their own terms, who have willingly repeated it; and what is this but a 'continuous progress' which broke off for fifteen or eighteen centuries? But for them, this consideration has not disturbed them!

Speaking more seriously, it is hard to agree that 'general civilisation' has benefited from the establishment of the Turk in Constantinople; and, in earlier times, when Sparta defeated Athens, I believe firmly that this made things worse.

But for the principle commonly accepted, 'nothing is lost or created', when this would be physically true, what has not at all been demonstrated, metaphysical truth is of another order, human truth, and changes there equate to real gains and real losses, which one knows not to name otherwise. If the genius, for example, was no more than a 'neurotic' and if genius transforms itself in the son of a Tasso or a Rousseau into epilepsy, shall one not say that something has been 'lost' from father to son? But on the contrary, and the case is frequent, who will say that there is no 'gain', when from the meeting of a 'war commissioner' and a girl a Dalembert is born? Will not the reader, once alerted to the idea, find in his memory as many examples as he wishes?

[43] *Evolution and the Origin of Species* by T. H. Huxley. French edition; Paris, 1892, J.-B. Baillière, p. 80, 81. (From the 1864 article, On criticisms of Mr Darwin's book.) (Original English of Huxley used here with Brunetière's italics.)

words of the notable physiologist who is renewing the notion of heredity. 'When one speaks of development in the animal or vegetable kingdoms,' writes Mr Weismann, 'one thinks, more often than not, of a development from lower form to higher, going on without interruption. *That is not the reality*. Regression plays here a very important role, and, *to consider properly the phenomena of retrogression, they permit us, almost more than those of the forward march,* to penetrate into the causes that determine the transformations of living nature.'[44] And to demonstrate clearly that man himself does not escape the reach of this law, Mr Herbert Spencer has told us, in his turn, 'that, in the loneliness of Australia as in the forests of the west of America, the Anglo-Saxon race, where our civilisation has developed elevated feelings to a high degree, *lowers itself rapidly towards relative barbarism*; it adopts the moral code and, sometimes, the habits of the savages'.[45]

24. I hope I may be permitted not to multiply uselessly the witnesses, and if Mr Spenser is perhaps no more than a philosopher, I think that the authority of Mr Weismann and Professor Huxley is not to be challenged. They are both 'scientists'! Not only has progress neither necessity nor continuity, not only does it never occur without compensation, but it is often just 'backwards'. I recall a word of Madame de Staël: 'This Revolution', she wrote, almost a century ago in 1798, 'can in the end light the way for a huge number of people, but over several years the coarseness of language, manners and opinions must make taste and reason go backwards in many regards.' Would one say

that she spoke only of 'literature' or 'philosophy'? But since her, and to the extent that the event clears itself up in the light of its consequences, do I need to recall the words of Émile Montégut[46], Taine or Mr Paul Bourget? 'We must undo the murderous work of the French Revolution. That is the advice which, for the impartial observer, comes out of all the comments made on the USA… It is the violent severing of all the historic ties between our past and our present that has so profoundly dried up the sources of our French vitality.' So concludes the author of *Outre-mer* [*Overseas or impressions of America* by Bourget]. And, in truth, as I have done elsewhere against Taine himself, I willingly defend the Revolution and its works against Mr Bourget.[47] However, when so many observers, 'coming from such different doctrines and with methods still more different', have raised the question, it is a proof at least that it exists and that there is a place to consider it. Do we then back away perhaps when we are priding ourselves on advancing? And believing ourselves to do what we wish, do we keep ourselves perhaps where we do not want to be? The past that we would abolish, is it worth more than the present, and above all the future that we feel threatened by? This is what the analogies of the evolutionary doctrine permitted us a short while ago, and it is what we must ask ourselves. Since a 'gradual progress towards perfection is very far from being a necessary part of the Darwinian theory' and since it can be said that evolution 'is perfectly compatible with a gradual retrogression'[48], the theory of progress, which has no basis in history, has no more of one in natural

---

[44]   *Essays on Heredity*, A. M. Weismann (French edition, translated by Mr Henry de Varigny; Paris, 1892, Reinwald, p. 381. This is the start of a conference on *Regression in Nature*.

[45]   Herbert Spencer, *Principles of Biology*, French edition translated by Mr Cazelles, vol. 1, p. 231. Cf. Quatrefages, *les Précurseurs de Darwin*; Paris, 1860, Germer-Baillière.

[46]   See the *Revue des Deux-Mondes* of 15 August 1871: *Où est la Révolution française?*

[47]   But I would not take the same line today as ten or twelve years ago; and I stress above all the reasons that Tocqueville has sketched in his *Ancien Régime*, and which Edgard Quinet, after him, has developed in his *Révolution*. I insist also on the point that most of the remonstrations that it is fashionable today to make against the Revolution strike through means of that former regime itself that they claim the Revolution destroyed.

[48]   Phrases of Mr Huxley in the article already cited.

history. It is in the air, so to speak; and from the rash confidence which our fathers have placed on it, nothing remains for us but to repair the disastrous effects.

25. I do not wish to speak, after all that, of either the slowness or the instability of progress, but how shall I not say a word of the theories which tend to deny 'the inheritance of acquired characteristics'? They teach us that, in nature as in humanity, neither mutilations nor truly individual acquisitions seem to be transmitted. A son does not inherit the 'science' or the 'erudition' of his father. The new generation is not necessarily, nor indeed ordinarily armed, it is not naturally armed, with all the resources of the former; and the greatest part of the path that the fathers have made, the children must make it or remake it in their turn. It would not be necessary to 'bring us up' or to 'teach' if matters were otherwise![49] But what transmits itself is the content of nature, so to speak; it is the general capability which serves at the same time as the physiological basis for trueness to type, and the means for individual development; and if man is not more than an animal struggling against his own instincts, this is what remains to us of which we may say: there is no 'progress, more worthy of the name than 'moral progress'.

26. Or rather, and making a better point, every kind of progress, scientific or industrial, exists only and has reason to exist only as a 'function' of moral progress.

'Have you sold your wheat, your herd and your wine? Are you free? Are the laws obeyed?'

[*As-tu vendu ton blé, ton bétail et ton vin? Es-tu libre? Les lois sont-elles respectées?*]

wrote a great poet [Alfred de Musset 1838, recalling Deuteronomy] long ago, – who, by a strange irony, nature has lodged in the soul of the most bourgeois of men[50], -, and, true child of his time, he dared to add: 'If we have all that, the rest is nothing.'

[*Si nous avons cela, le reste est peu de chose!!*]

27. Indeed no! The remainder is not nothing! And, to the contrary, it is what is left that matters. What matters is for us to remember the solidarity which binds us and to which our first duty is to sacrifice something of our individualism or our egoism. What matters is to work as hard as we can for the realisation of justice among men. And what matters, and what must be the sovereign law of our activities, is to contribute on our individual part to the perfection of the species; itself defined, as we have seen, by the 'theory of inheritance'! We fight over the matter, where we have too great a tendency to fall on our own weight; – to put the object of life outside of life itself, and not without doubt to make a 'meditation on death', but, in the consideration of death and suffering, to seek, to find, to sustain the ineradicable basis, the metaphysical foundations, and real however, of equality among men[51]; to restore in the contemporary world (such as we have made it: revolutionary individualism, science including the evil and industrialism to excess) that solidarity of which our politicians, after having strangely misunderstood it when they were in office, make, today when they are not, this astonishing discovery[52]... if there has formerly been just a sketch of morality, the lineaments are here now, still vague, but already visible, of a law of history, which starts to clear itself

---

[49] See Weismann: *Essais sur l'hérédité*, and W.-P. Ball: *Hérédité et exercice*, Paris, 1891; Lecrosnier et Babé.

[50] This is hardly the place to expatiate on Alfred de Musset, but I say what I want to say when I call him in passing 'the most bourgeois of men'; and some day perhaps I shall find occasion to justify a judgement here excessive in its brevity.

[51] See once more, in this connexion, Bourdalue, in the sermon already cited on *Thoughts about death*, and Schopenhauer.

[52] I have no reason to conceal the fact that, in writing this, I dream of Mr Léon Bourgeois who, to occupy his leisure last Winter, showed us, in the *Nouvelle Revue*, I believe, the merits of solidarity. But he forgot one point, that we ourselves, like him, indeed before him, have believed, I certainly cannot assert, in 'the religion of humanity' but in the possibility of establishing a morality on the basis of solidarity; and what we have stopped believing; and what between positivism or Comte-ism and what we ask permission to call the new idealism, the whole debate is there.

of the evolutionary theory. *Sic nos, non nobis* [thus we work, but not for ourselves. Virgil] ... we are not born for ourselves, nor precisely for others, but, now and in the future, to work all together towards a common task, which is to free ourselves from slavery to our own nature. That alone counts; to that alone is it worthy to dedicate ourselves; that alone permits us to realise our true selves, at an historic moment, or to approach from afar the perfection of our species; and that alone, I believe I can now say, since one wants 'science', conforms to the data of evolutionary theory. It remains to me to make visible what one can expect or hope from the theory for the restoration of a metaphysics of which one is too hasty to say that it will have pronounced the sentence.

III

28. Finally, what reintegrates evolutionary theory into science, and what substitutes there for the idea of a blind 'mechanism', is the idea or above all the muffled foreboding of a certain order, an order as it were motivated and intelligent, which directs, according to certain laws, the government of the universe[53]. This is what was recognised by the man who before Darwin did the most for the 'theory of descent [with modification]', and it has to be said: the man whose theories have reconquered some time ago all the territory lost by pure Darwinism. 'The ladder of life', wrote Lamarck, in his *Philosophie zoologique*, 'represents the order that belongs to nature and which results, as much as do the objects that brought about that order,

from means that have been received from the supreme author of everything...' He then develops technical considerations and finishes thus: 'By wise precautions, everything maintains the established order; the changes and the perpetual renewals which are observed in that order are maintained within the boundaries which they do not exceed; the races of living beings remain altogether despite their variations; the progress achieved in the improvement of organisation is hardly lost; *everything that seems disordered, upside down, anomalous, returns ceaselessly to the general order and indeed there is concord*; and above all and always the will of the sublime author of nature and all that exists is invariably carried out.'[54] Dare I say that whoever does not accept these conclusions of Lamarck and who does not see the tight, logical and necessary relationship with the theory of animal variability, is it that theory, is it the 'theory of descent [with modification]', is it the theory of evolution itself which he means or he does not mean? Essentially and fundamentally, so to speak, the evolutionary theory is no more than a *theology*, as the philosophers say; and its organisation is only possibly by means of and through the agency of the idea of *finality*[55].

29. One knows the jeering that Bacon and our philosophers of the 18th century, one after the other, believed they could direct against the search for *final causes*. Have they then not seen that there are at least two ways to conceive of final causes? And, in this regard, do we accuse them of absent-mindedness or unfairness? What they have pretended to believe, in any case, is

---

[53] If it was not in the destiny of general ideas to survive because of what they have engendered, a single observation could serve as all that development, and here it is: the *final cause*, expelled from science by a purely mechanical explication of the universe, must necessarily return with biology.

[54] Lamarck, *Zoological Philosophy*, vol. 1, pp. 113–114, edition Ch. Martins.

[55] Mr Huxley, from the beginning, or almost from the beginning, in 1864, in his On criticisms of Mr Darwin's book, had tried hard to defend the author against 'reproach'; because he had been reproached, above all in Germany. But since then, Mr von Hartmann, in his *Philosophy of the Unconscious*, which has been attacked as much for its pessimism, to tell the truth, as for its 'idealist' tendency, and in a pamphlet written expressly on *Darwinism, what is true and what false in this theory* (Paris, 1880, Germer Baillière), has reopened the question. He has simply proved that, if the philosophers are not always up with the latest science, the scientists also sometimes need, before they talk metaphysics, an initiation into what they lack.

that search for the final cause relates solely to pleasure or to human utility[56]; and, starting from this principle, they have hardly been able to establish firmly that neither 'noses are made to wear spectacles', nor 'fingers to be adorned with rings', nor 'legs to wear silk trousers' is true. They would have less readily established that the eyes are not made to see; Voltaire, who had good sense, in fact made this remark several times. But the Baconians of his time were stronger![57] And when after that our own physicists or chemists have come in their turn, as they have hardly had to show, they no more, that the combinations of carbon and hydrogen, or the laws of 'falling bodies', they have no immediate relationship to the duty or the consent of man, it's more than ever so, with more assurance and confidence, that the words of the former Lord Chancellor of England are repeated: investigation of final causes is sterile, just as a virgin consecrated to God produces nothing. [*Causarum finalium inquisitio sterilis est, et tanquam virgo Deo consecrata, nihil parit.*] This is what one says, in a more up to date way, in saying that science enquires only into the 'how' of things, never into the 'why'.[58]

30. I do not think that there was ever a more disastrous error! Not only is the question of 'why' opium puts one to sleep confounded with the question 'how', the two questions are really just one; but what evolutionary theory establishes, or implies, is that one knows the 'how' of the variations or transformations of animals to the extent that one concerns oneself with the investigation of the 'why'.

31. If we wish to convince ourselves, quite simply reverse the spiritual jokes of the Encyclopaedists, and ask ourselves if 'silk trousers' are not made to dress legs? Rings to ornament fingers? 'Spectacles' to relieve the eyes? And what is that meant to say: that 'spectacles' are made for eyes? That is aimed at saying that one need know nothing of the details of the manufacture of spectacles, or the reason for their shape, or their properties of their defects generally, if one does not know their purpose. The true idea of a 'final cause' is thus that of the collection or adaptation of a set of means to a predetermined end; or, if you wish, it is the idea of an end that can only be attained by certain means, which it determines; and is not the idea the same in evolution? I would like here to believe Claude Bernard: 'In every living embryo, there is a creative idea which develops and manifests itself through organisation... Here, as everywhere, all derives from the idea which alone creates and directs; the means of expression are common to the whole of nature, and stay mixed up higgledy-piggledy, like the letters of the alphabet, in a box *where a force will find them to express the most varied thoughts or mechanisms.*' He also said: 'The physicist and the chemist, not being able to put themselves outside the universe, study the body and its properties... without being obliged to relate them to nature as a whole. However, the physiologist, finding himself to the contrary located outside the animal of which he sees the whole, must take account of the harmony of the whole organism. *From which it follows that the*

---

[56] Note on this subject that if man is certainly not 'master of creation' and the earth is not 'centre of the world', nothing is more indifferent in practice; and above all in the case of morality or 'sociology'.

[57] It could be a useful exercise to trace the influence of Bacon on French thought. It had hardly started in the middle of the 18th century, with the Encyclopaedists, when they made of the author of *Novum Organum* the God that the preceding century had made of Descartes. He remained for almost fifty years the master of their minds; and it was Joseph de Maistre, with his usual perspicacity, who, in his war against the spirit of the 18th century, gathered his forces and directed them against Bacon. Through eclecticism, so as not to be suspected of thinking like the author of *Pope (Pape)* and the *French Church (Eglise Gallicane)* [*Du Pape suivi de l'Église Gallicane dans son Rapport avec le Souverain Pontiff*, 1838, Brussels], one can admire still in Bacon the 'lawmaker of induction'. And his authority succumbed at last in the second half of the 19th century to that of Liebig and Claude Bernard.

[58] See the article *la Science idéale et la Science positive* in *Revue des Deux-Mondes* for 15 November 1863.

physicists and the chemist can omit any idea of final causes in the facts that they observe, while the physiologist is forced to admit an harmonious and pre-existing finality in the organism.' And further still, in the last of his great works: 'Physical agents produce phenomena that they do not control: *the vital force controls phenomena that it does not produce.*'[59] This is the origin of what is today called '*neo-vitalism*'. But one could not more precisely affirm that a superior finality – transcendent or immanent, it matters not today – presides over the expression of the vital force, as in the evolution of organised matter, as in the transformation of animal species, and guides it. No variation has sufficient reason in the exercise or the disuse of parts, in the demands of adaptation to the environment, in the set of causes still less known that we wrap up with the label *natural selection*, but that we find in these phenomena the interior drive of an organism towards the realisation of an organic plan set down in advance. The realisation of this 'organic plan' is the final cause of evolution.

32. May we bring out the consequences? 'We do not ask if the dog, if the horse, if the ox has been created for man, but if the structure of these animals reveals an *intention*?'[60] We can answer boldly: there is in the germ an *intention* to conform to the species type; there is in the appearance of a variant an *intention* to adapt to a plan; and there is in nature an *intention* for all beginnings to head for a preset destination. What is this to say, if not that, just as the 'theory of descent [with modification]' has already allowed us to give a physiological meaning to the dogma of original sin, now, on the basis of evolutionary theory, we can resurrect the idea of Providence! I do not here mean that Providence, particularly the Christian concept, which reveals its choices in 'chance events', that personal Providence, without the consent or intervention of which not a 'hair on one's head' would fall. Of that Providence the understanding is less

rich! But I want to say that general Providence, which better to distinguish it, I shall call philosophical or pagan, the Providence of the Stoics:

The spirit within nourishes, and the mind diffused throughout living nature animates the whole and mingles with the vastness of the universe [*Spiritus intus alit, totamque infusa per artus /Mens agitat molem… Aeneid,* Virgil]

33. That Providence, finally, which is no more than the personification of the organic plan that we have just been discussing – not only us, but Claude Bernard, if I have forgotten to say that this is his expression. Against the rigid and unintelligent 'mechanism' with which modern free thought has too long been content, if evolutionary theory has not 'demonstrated' – as it has not, I fear – the existence of such a Providence, it certainly has suggested its existence. And so, by one of those frequent ironies, those who proclaim the theory most bigotedly, those who have nothing but evolution and inheritance in their mouths, those who believe the 'official' representatives of the theory, they are the most clearly for their narrowness of spirit… and their hatred of anything new (the 'misoneism' of Cesare Lombroso).

34. Because it will vainly be objected that this idea is no more than the classical idea of the final cause, which was formulated by Bernardin de Saint-Pierre, and which these good people continue to do and to sustain carefully, in order to be able to ridicule it more easily! One has always the right – provided that we give warning – to modify, to correct, to improve the usual definitions of things; and just the same must we not act, to the extent that they help to design things better, even things better understood? I could quote twenty definitions of species or genus, living or dead, which, each in its time, has expressed an advance corresponding to the physiology of that time. At the same time, evolutionary theory is bringing about effects that Haeckel and Spencer did not expect in quick

---

[59] Claude Bernard, *Introduction to experimental medicine* [in French], p. 162, 153, 154; and *Lessons on the phenomena of life common to plants and animals* [in French], vol. 1, p. 51.

[60] Jóseph de Maistre, *Examination of the philosophy of Bacon* [in French].

succession. 'By what sign', a philosopher once asked, 'can one recognise *finality*, and how does one distinguish it from *causality*? When existing facts, rigorously observed, suffice to explain a phenomenon entirely, the explanation is causal. When established facts are insufficient, and must appeal to something which has not been completely fulfilled, or which will so be only in the future... the explanation is more or less final.'[61] Such is the idea of finality that is produced today by all those who have not remained 'in their old Sorbonne notebooks', as Renan said disdainfully of all those who did not share his opinions. And that idea engenders another, one which I have myself expressed too often not to take pleasure today in borrowing from the same author: 'Zoological laws have not been reduced to physico-chemical laws... Evolutionism introduces the idea of historical law... Courtesy of this new kind of law... we distance ourselves more and more from the kind of necessity... Things are variable in their natures and laws unite here the always changing goals amongst them.'[62] To our eyes this is indeed true? There are no 'iron laws' in the living world, but simply principles, complex, general and supple principles, so to speak, flexible in various senses; principles of which the applications are in turn multiple, diverse and changing; and principles of which the formula, without being loose in this regard, is always at least indeterminate and as open by some place.[63] I want to insist on this first, though indeed the question merits a much deeper study; and I am content today to have shown what might be the metaphysical, historical and moral fecundity of the theory of evolution.

35. I expect, on this conclusion, that the evolutionists will reproach me for having arbitrarily interpreted the theory that they believe they have care of. It is the custom today to think, when we think, if I can put it this way, in terms of 'whole systems of ideas'; and as long as you have once invoked the name Darwin, you have given orders no longer to think, one after the other, on the trail, in the steps of Darwin. But when it would not be too easy to contrast, and how to bang the evolutionists' heads together[64], I respond still with what cannot too often be repeated: we know that every 'system' is wrong as such; it is destructive as a system; and there are never more than fragments that are good. 'Each makes his own little religion for himself,' said that good princess; and I simply claim the right to have also 'my little evolution for myself'. If I have thus not argued wrongly, if I have not used awkwardly any of the assumptions on which the 'theory of descent [with modification]'(like any theory) rests; and if I have not moreover questioned any of the 'facts' which natural history has 'scientifically' established, this is enough; the rest is unimportant. 'Science, which is not infallible, unfortunately, either in observation of facts, or in their interpretation, is probably even less reliable in the inferences drawn from it. This is indeed why its conclusions say absolutely nothing about morality or metaphysics; – as is proved by the

---

[61] *On the idea of natural law in contemporary science and philosophy* [in French], by Mr Émile Boutroux; Paris, 1895, Lecène et Oudin, p. 97.

[62] Ibid, Pp. 101, 102.

[63] Other progress that is owed to biological science, or –if we are not to speak of 'progress'- another remarkable example of transformation that has been effected in the general method! 'We do not share his scepticism,' said Royer-Collard long ago; and since then we have had to realise, to the contrary, that 'we must believe where we believe, and doubt where we doubt'. Between absolute doubt and complete certainty, there are not just degrees, but truly it is in between doubt and certainty that human opinions move, so to speak. There are degrees of *necessity*. This is what we have learnt of the so-called natural sciences, of which the laws are laws also, but sharing none of the strictness of physical or mathematical laws.

[64] I reflect, on this point, on the last book of Quatrefages: *The emulators of Darwin* [in French], 2 vols octavo; Paris, 1894, Alcan.

example of enough great scientists, if I am not mistaken[65].

36. But, on the other hand, what one could say, and indeed I say it myself, is that the *Descent of Man* of Darwin, or the *Natural History of Creation* by Professor Haeckel, are to give them their true name, no more than scientific novels. It has not been 'proved' that animal species vary, nor above all that they are transformed, one into another; it has not been 'proved' that the 'struggle for existence' or 'natural selection' are anything but big words; and it has not been 'proved' that man is descended from an animal. Mr Russel Wallace, as I have pointed out, has always maintained the contrary; and, in affirming that appearances are *as if* we descended from monkeys, he has continued to teach that we are not. In these conditions, what is then the theory of evolution? It is a simply hypothesis, or, better, a *method*. It is a means of classifying or organising from one point of view facts or ideas which would otherwise escape us and which seduce us, so to speak, by the ease of our capture. It is a means to achieve clarity. It is a means to penetrate more deeply into the facts themselves and to discover new ones. What is a method is also a discipline for the mind which creates naturally a general habit, a new way of thinking. And in that sense, with a little exaggeration, Huxley could have said that 'for anyone studying the signs of the times, the appearance of the theory of evolution was…

the most miraculous event of the 19th century'. As the comparative method had done before it, the evolutionary or 'genealogical' method renewed the face of science[66]. Another (the fiery Haeckel) has said that 'From now on we shall assess the intelligence of men according to the greater or less ease with which they accept the theory of evolution'; and in this form the idea has something in truth more ridiculous still than impertinent. But it is no less certain that, for forty years, it is not only the domain of science, it is the domain of philosophy which the theory of evolution seems to have transformed completely. This is what we needed – in that series of studies where we wished, at the same time as our examination of our conscience, to make the same study as that of some of our contemporaries – the obligation to consider some of the consequences of the theory; and this is what I have tried to do.

37. And we admit, moreover, that (as we had warned the reader) it is not from within, but from without, from the clarity of the moral law, that we have considered evolutionary theory. The morality that one can draw from evolutionary theory will never be more than a kind of 'refracted' morality, of which we always have to seek elsewhere the origin or the source of illumination. Our animal descent, should it be proven, would not create real 'duties' for us; and the consequences our deeds can have for the future of the species will never be a real

---

[65]   This is not the least of the dangers that the superstition of science causes us. When we have used thirty years of our life to study the history of literature or of art, we cannot call ourselves qualified to decide a point of naval tactics or administrative law; rightly, I think! But the competence of a physicist or a physiologist can easily be regarded as universal; and if he has made some discovery in that science – in which chance can have as great a part as inspiration, but which seizes the imagination -, his credit can increase without limit. In truth, the profession of scientist confers holy unction. And yet, being human, they can quarrel, but they are careful not to *criticise* each other, one can foresee, now, where this will lead us one day. They are already a 'brotherhood'; but they could become a 'caste', like mandarins; and the dream of Renan would be realised. Scientists would become kings, and to ensure their necessary leisure for the invention of 'aerial navigation' or 'nourishing tablets', the rest of humanity would have work to exhaustion. I am among those for whom railways and steamships are enough! And I will not serve my sentence to maintain a Prytanée [military school] to keep the 'scientists' fat.

[66]   'As great as must be the interest that attaches to biological history isolated from living beings,' said Mr Balfour, '*that interest has been increased tenfold* by the generalisations of Darwin.' One could say as much of the related studies of palaeontology.

'sanction'. But is it not something to have been forced by the theory of evolution into a fresh examination of the problem of morality? If, on the other hand, we had established that the hypothesis or theory was not incompatible, or indeed that it seemed to agree internally with the moral doctrine, of which one has sometimes feared that it had shaken the foundations, that would be so much more. Finally, if we have shown that outside of moral progress, all 'progress' is no more than an illusion or a chimaera, and that this is the teaching of evolutionary theory, would we not have been rewarded enough for the time and trouble that we have taken? We must not ask of things more than they can give; and since the first foundation of all morality is to recognise that man, as a man, is certainly placed in nature 'like an empire within an empire' [Spinoza's saying], that would not be a result so despicable as to have wrung the confession out of science as out of nature.

The End

Biographical note on Brunetière

Ferdinand Brunetière was born in Toulon on 19 July 1849 and died in Paris 9 December 1906. He was educated at the Lycée Louis-le-Grand. He took part as an infantryman in the Franco-Prussian war.

He worked as a teacher in Paris and tried his hand at journalism, which proved a great success: from writing for the *Revue des Deux Mondes*, he became a prominent literary critic and polemicist, then editor of this influential journal in 1893. He had been a professor at the École Normale Supérieure (ENS) from 1886, and held this position until 1905. According to the Catholic Encyclopaedia (Anon., n.d.), 'he was dropped from the list of professors' '[o]n account of his conversion to Catholicism'. According to Shurts (2013), it was on account of his prominence as an anti-Dreyfusard in the aftermath of the Dreyfus case; she notes that he was 'the only professor not incorporated into the Sorbonne from the ENS' when the Sorbonne was reorganised in 1905. The Academie Française, to which he was elected in 1893 (seat 28), in its biography of Brunetière records that he was 'professeur à la Sorbonne'. (Academie Française, n.d.).

Brunetière published many major works of literary criticism, notably *l'Évolution des genres dans l'histoire de la literature*, regarded as an important work of literary theory.

Butler (2016) gives an account of Brunetière's attempt to 'strike a balance between age-old moral commandments and the practical demands of modernity'.

References:

Academie Française, (n.d.) Ferdinand Brunetière http://www.academie-francaise.fr/les-immortels/ferdinand-brunetiere (accessed 24 January 2017)

Adamczyk, M., U. Ambrosius, S. Lietzenmaier, A. Wichniak, F. Holsboer, and E. Friess, 2015, Genetics of rapid eye movement sleep in humans: Translational Psychiatry, **5**, no. 7, e598, accessed 27 June 2017. 10.1038/tp.2015.85 PMID 26151926

Aissouni, Y., El Guerrab, A., Hamieh, A. M., Ferrier, J., Chalus, M., Lemaire, D., Grégoire, S., Etienne, M., EschalierA., Ardid, D., Lingueglia, E. and Marchand, F. 2017 Acid-Sensing Ion Channel 1a in the amygdala is involved in pain and anxiety-related behaviours associated with arthritis. Scientific Reports | 7:43617 | DOI: 10.1038/srep43617 (accessed 9 March 2017).

Alekseyenko, O. V., Y. B. Chan, R. Li, and E. A. Kravitz, 2013, Single dopaminergic neurons that modulate aggression in Drosophila: Proceedings of the National Academy of Sciences of the United States of America, **110**, no. 15, 6151–6156. 10.1073/pnas.1303446110 PMID 23530210

Amoore, J. E., 1967, Specific anosmia: a clue to the olfactory code: Nature, **214**, no. 5093, 1095–1098. 10.1038/2141095a0 PMID 4861233

Andrews, P., 2015, An Ape's View of Human Evolution: Cambridge University Press. 10.1017/CBO9781316180938

Anonymous, n.d. Ferdinand Brunetière http://www.catholic.org/encyclopedia/view.php?id=2225 (accessed 24 January 2017)

Anonymous, 2016, Refugee and migrant crisis: the deficient global response: Lancet, **388**, 633 DOI: http://dx.doi.org/10.1016/S0140–6736(16)31342–3. (accessed 25 November 2017). PMID:27533423

Apata, M., B. Arriaza, E. Llop, and M. Moraga, 2017, Human adaptation to arsenic in Andean populations of the Atacama Desert: American Journal of Physical Anthropology, **163**, no. 1, 192–199, accessed 3 March 2017. 10.1002/ajpa.23193 PMID 28206677

Apps, M. A. J., Grima, L. L., Manohar, S. and Husain, M. 2015 The role of cognitive effort in subjective reward devaluation and risky decision-making. Scientific Reports | 5:16880 | DOI: 10.1038/srep16880

Araji, S., 2000 Review essay – A Natural History of Rape Biological bases of sexual coercion. Alaska Justice Forum 17 2–3.

Arnqvist, G., and M. Kirkpatrick, 2005, The evolution of infidelity in socially monogamous passerines: the strength of direct and indirect selection on extrapair copulation behavior in females: American Naturalist, **165**, no. S5, Suppl 5, S26–S37. 10.1086/429350 PMID 15795859

Arrhenius, S., 1896, On the influence of carbonic acid in the air upon the temperature of the ground: Philosophical Magazine and Journal of Science, **41**, no. 251, 237–276. 10.1080/14786449608620846

Australian Bureau of Statistics 2012 Suicides 4125.0 – Gender Indicators, Australia, Jan 2012. Canberra, ABS.

Avery, M., 2014, A Message from Martha The extinction of the Passenger Pigeon and its relevance today: Bloomsbury.

Babbage, C., 1830. *Reflections on the decline of science in England, and on some of its causes.* London. http://www.gutenberg.org/files/1216/1216-h/1216-h.htm (accessed 29 April 2016)

Bailey, J. M., M. P. Dunne, and N. G. Martin, 2000, Genetic and environmental influences on sexual orientation and its correlates in an Australian twin sample: Journal of Personality and Social Psychology, **78**, no. 3, 524–536. 10.1037/0022-3514.78.3.524 PMID 10743878

Barnes, E. W., 1924, Science and immortality, in J. Marchant, ed., Immortality: Putnam, 145–171.

Bauer, W. D., and U. Mathesius, 2004, Plant responses to bacterial quorum sensing signals: Current Opinion in Plant Biology, **7**, no. 4, 429–433. 10.1016/j.pbi.2004.05.008 PMID 15231266

Bem, D. J., 1996, Exotic becomes erotic: a developmental theory of sexual orientation: Psychological Review, **103**, no. 2, 320–335. 10.1037/0033-295X.103.2.320

Bentham, J. 1780, 1789, 1823. An Introduction to the Principles of Morals and Legislation.

Bergson, H. 1911 *Creative Evolution.*

Bertolote, J. M., and A. Fleischmann, 2002, A global perspective in the epidemiology of suicide: Suicidologi, **7**, 6–8.

Bishop, J. A., D. J. Hartley, and G. G. Partridge, 1977, The population dynamics of genetically determined resistance to warfarin in Rattus norvegicus from mid Wales: Heredity, **39**, no. 3, 389–398. 10.1038/hdy.1977.81 PMID 272364

Blokland, G. A. M., K. L. McMahon, P. M. Thompson, N. G. Martin, G. I.de Zubicaray, and M. J. Wright, 2011, Heritability of working memory brain activation: The Journal of Neuroscience : The Official Journal of the Society for Neuroscience, **31**, no. 30, 10882–10890. 10.1523/JNEUROSCI.5334-10.2011 PMID 21795540

Blows, M. W., and A. A. Hoffmann, 2005, A reassessment of genetic limits to evolutionary change: Ecology, **86**, no. 6, 1371–1384. 10.1890/04-1209

Bonnard, M., Chen, S., Gaychet, J., Carrere, M., Woodman, M., Guisiano, B. and Jirsa, V. 2016 Resting state brain dynamics and its transients: a combined TMS-EEG study. Scientific Reports | 6:31220 | DOI: 10.1038/srep31220 (accessed 5 September 2016)

Boomsma, D. I., G. Willemsen, C. V. Dolan, L. C. Hawkley, and J. T. Cacioppo, 2005, Genetic and environmental contributions to loneliness in adults: the Netherlands twin register study: Behavior Genetics, **35**, no. 6, 745–752. 10.1007/s10519-005-6040-8 PMID 16273322

Boswell, J., 1872, J. W. Croker and J. Wright, eds., 1791 *The Life of Samuel Johnson LLD.* (Citations from the 9 volume edition: Bell & Duldy.

Boudesseul, J., A. Lantian, F. Cova, and L. Bègue, 2016, Free love? On the relation between belief in free will, determinism, and passionate love: Consciousness and Cognition, **46**, 47–59. 10.1016/j.concog.2016.09.003 PMID 27677053

Brunetière, F., 1913, Les Raisons actuelles de Croire Discours prononcé à Lille le 18 novembre 1900, pour la cloture du 27° Congrès des Catholiques du Nord: Librairie Bloud et Cie.

Buades-Rotger, M., C. Brunnlieb, T. F. Münte, M. Heldmann, and U. M. Krämer, 2016, Winning is not enough: ventral striatum connectivity during physical aggression: Brain Imaging and Behavior, **10**, no. 1, 105–114. 10.1007/s11682-015-9370-z PMID 25759287

Buck, L. A., Unraveling the sense of smell. https://www.nobelprize.org/nobel_prizes/medicine/laureates/2004/buck-lecture.html (accessed 15 June 2017)

Butler, E., 2016 'Do you know Brunetière?' Fortnightly Review http://fortnightlyreview.co.uk/2016/06/butler-brunetiere/#fnref-16902–2 (accessed 12 June 2017)

Camus, A., 1989, *Selected Essays and Notebooks*. (Selected and edited by P. Thody): Penguin.

Careau, V., D. Thomas, M. M. Humphries, and D. Réale, 2008, Energy metabolism and animal personality: Oikos, **117**, no. 5, 641–653. 10.1111/j.0030-1299.2008.16513.x

Caspi, A., K. Sugden, T. E. Moffitt, A. Taylor, I. W. Craig, H. Harrington, J. McClay, J. Mill, J. Martin, A. Braithwaite, and R. Poulton, 2003, Influence of life stress on depression: moderation by a polymorphism in the 5-HTT gene: Science, **301**, no. 5631, 386–389. 10.1126/science.1083968 PMID 12869766

Catel, W. and Schmidt, J. 1959 Über familiäre gichtische Diathese in Verbindung mit zerebralen und renalen Symptomen bei einem Kleinkind. Deutsche medicinische Wochenschrift 84 2145–2147.

Cesarini, D., C. T. Dawes, J. H. Fowler, M. Johannesson, P. Lichtenstein, and B. Wallace, 2008, Heritability of cooperative behavior in the trust game: Proceedings of the National Academy of Sciences of the United States of America, **105**, no. 10, 3721–3726. 10.1073/pnas.0710069105 PMID 18316737

Changeux, J.-P., 2008, Du vrai, du beau, du bien. Une nouvelle approche neuronale: Odile Jacob.

Charlesworth, B., 2000, Fisher, Medawar, Hamilton and the evolution of aging: Genetics, **156**, no. 3, 927–931. PMID 11063673

Cherkas, L. F., E. C. Oelsner, Y. T. Mak, A. Valdes, and T. D. Spector, 2004, Genetic influences on female infidelity and number of sexual partners in humans: a linkage and association study of the role of the vasopressin receptor gene (AVPR1A): Twin Research, **7**, no. 6, 649–658. 10.1375/twin.7.6.649 PMID 15607016

Chomsky, N. and McGilvray, J. The Science of Language: interviews with James McGilvray. Cambridge University Press. 10.1017/CBO9781139061018

Coyne, J. A., 2009, Why Evolution is True: Oxford University Press.

Cronin, H., 1992, The Ant and the Peacock: Cambridge University Press.

Cubitt, T. S., D. Perez-Garcia, and M. M. Wolf, 2015, Undecidability of the spectral gap: Nature, **528**, no. 7581, 207–211. 10.1038/nature16059 PMID 26659181

Curtis, J., and C. F. Curtis, 1985, Homostyle primroses re-visited. I. Variation in time and space: Heredity, **54**, no. 2, 227–234. 10.1038/hdy.1985.30

Cyranoski, D., 2017, China's push for better babies: Nature, **548**, 272–274. 10.1038/548272a PMID 28816265

Daiches Raphael, D. 1958 Darwinism and ethics. Pp. 334-359 in *A Century of Darwin*. (Ed. S. A. Barnett). London, Heinemann

Darwin, C. R., 1859, On the Origin of Species by Means of Natural Selection, or the preservation of favoured races in the struggle for life. London, John Murray.

Darwin, C. R., 1862/1904 The Various Contrivances by which Orchids are Fertilised by Insects. (7th impression of 2nd edition) London, John Murray.

Darwin, C. R., 1871/1901, The Descent of Man and Selection in Relation to Sex, 2nd ed.: John Murray.

Darwin, C. R., 1872, The Expression of the Emotions in Man and Animals: John Murray. 10.1037/10001-000

Darwin, C. R. F., 1903–5, Darwin and A. C. Seward, eds., More Letters of Charles Darwin a record of his work in a series of hitherto unpublished letters, **v. 2**: John Murray, 52.

Davis, D. J., Doerr, H. M., Grzelak, A. K., Busi, S. B., Jasarevic, E., Ericsson, A. C. & Bryda, E. C. 2016 Lactobacillus plantarum attenuates anxiety-related behavior and protects against stress-induced dysbiosis in adult zebrafish. Scientific Reports | 6:33726 | DOI: 10.1038/srep33726 (accessed 23 September 2016)

Dawkins, R., 1976, The Selfish Gene: Oxford University Press.

de Duve, C., 2009a *Génétique du péché original le poids du passé sur l'avenir de la vie*. Paris, Odile Jacob. (English translation de Duve, C. 2010. Genetics of Original Sin: The Impact of Natural Selection on the Future of Humanity. (with Neil Patterson). New Haven, CN, Yale University Press.)

de Duve, C., 2009b, The future of life. Scientific Insights into the Evolution of the Universe and of Life Pontifical Academy of Sciences: Acta, **20**, 2009, accessed 5 February 2016, www.pas.va/content/dam/accademia/pdf/acta20/acta20-deduve.pdf.

Delitz, H., 2011, Arnold Gehlen: UVK.

Dennett, D. C., 1995, Darwin's Dangerous Idea Evolution and the meanings of life. New York, Simon & Schuster

Dennis, A. R., and J. S. Valacich, 1994, Group, sub-group, and nominal group idea generation: new rules for a new media?: Journal of Management, **20**, no. 4, 723–736. 10.1177/014920639402000402

DeSteno, D. A., and P. Salovey, 1996, Evolutionary origin of sex differences in jealousy? Questioning the 'fitness' of the model: Psychological Science, **7**, no. 6, 367–374. 10.1111/j.1467-9280.1996.tb00391.x

Diaz Heijtz, R., Wang, S., Anuar, F., Qiana, Y., Björkholm, B., Samuelsson, A., Hibberd, M. L., Forssberg, H. and Pettersson, S. 2011 Normal gut microbiota modulates brain development and behaviour. PNAS | February 15, 2011 | vol. 108 | no. 7 | 3047–3052 (accessed 31 March 2017)

Donaldson, Z. R., and L. J. Young, 2008, Oxytocin, vasopressin, and the neurogenetics of sociality: Science, **322**, no. 5903, 900–904. 10.1126/science.1158668 PMID 18988842

Dotsch, R., Hassin, R. R. and Todorov, A. 2016 Statistical learning shapes face evaluation. Nature Human Behaviour 1, 1–6. | DOI: 10.1038/s41562-016-0001 (accessed 31 May 2017)

Doyle, A. C., 1892, The Memoirs of Sherlock Holmes: John Murray.

Duncan, C. J., and P. M. Sheppard, 1963, Continuous and quantal theories of sensory discrimination: Proceedings of the Royal Society of London. Series B, Biological Sciences, **158**, no. 972, 343–363. 10.1098/rspb.1963.0052 PMID 14070050

Dunn, R. R., N. C. Harris, R. K. Colwell, L. P. Koh, and N. S. Sodhi, 2009, The sixth mass coextinction: are most endangered species parasites and mutualists?: Proceedings. Biological Sciences, **276**, no. 1670, 3037–3045. 10.1098/rspb.2009.0413 PMID 19474041

Eaves, L., H. J. Eysenck, and N. G. Martin, 1989, Genes, Culture and Personality: Academic Press.

Edwards, D. P., 2009, The roles of tolerance in the evolution, maintenance and breakdown of mutualism: Naturwissenschaften, **96**, no. 10, 1137–1145, accessed 2 June 2017. 10.1007/s00114-009-0559-0 PMID 19484212

Edwards, J. H., 1993 The Galton Lecture for 1991: numeracy and innumeracy in genetics. Pp. 75–90 in Sir Francis Galton FRS the legacy of his ideas. Proceedings of the 28th annual symposium of the Galton Institute, London, 1991. (Ed. M. Keynes). London Macmillan.

Enard, W., M. Przeworski, S. E. Fisher, C. S. L. Lai, V. Wiebe, T. Kitano, A. P. Monaco, and S. Pääbo, 2002, Molecular evolution of *FOXP2*, a gene involved in speech and language: Nature, **418**, no. 6900, 869–872. 10.1038/nature01025 PMID 12192408

Fadel, F. R., P. Driscoll, M. Pilot, H. Wright, H. Zulch and D. Mills, 2016. Differences in trait impulsivity indicate diversification of dog breeds into working and show lines. Scientific Reports 6, Article number: 22162 (2016) doi; 10.1038/srep22162 (Accessed 27 November 2017)

Fain, B., 2008. Evolution and providence, pp. 427–446 in Seckbach, J. and Gordon, R. (Eds) 2008 Divine Action and Natural Selection Science, Faith and Evolution. World Scientific Publishing Co., Singapore.

Feldman, M. W., and L. Eshel, 1982, On the theory of parent-offspring conflict: a two-locus model: American Naturalist, **119**, no. 2, 285–292. 10.1086/283909

Ferguson, B. J., and U. Mathesius, 2014, Phytohormone regulation of legume-rhizobia interactions: Journal of Chemical Ecology, **40**, no. 7, 770–790. 10.1007/s10886-014-0472-7 PMID 25052910

Ferriere, R., J. L. Bronstein, S. Rinaldi, R. Law, and M. Gauduchon, 2002, Cheating and the evolutionary stability of mutualisms: Proceedings. Biological Sciences, **269**, no. 1493, 773–780. 10.1098/rspb.2001.1900 PMID 11958708

Fiegna, F., and G. J. Velicer, 2003, Competitive fates of bacterial social parasites: persistence and self-induced extinction of *Myxococcus xanthus* cheaters: Proceedings. Biological Sciences, **270**, no. 1523, 1527–1534. 10.1098/rspb.2003.2387 PMID 12965020

Fisher, D. O., C. R. Dickman, M. E. Jones, and S. P. Blomberg, 2013 Sperm competition drives the evolution of suicidal reproduction in mammals. 17910–17914 | PNAS | October 29, 2013 | vol. 110 www.pnas.org/cgi/doi/10.1073/pnas.1310691110

Fisher, R. A., 1914, Some hopes of a eugenist: The Eugenics Review, **5**, no. 4, 309–315. PMID 21259575

Fisher, R. A., 1918, On the correlation between relatives on the supposition of Mendelian inheritance: Transactions of the Royal Society of Edinburgh, **52**, no. 02, 399–433. 10.1017/S0080456800012163

Fisher, R. A., 1922, The evolution of the conscience in civilised communities: In special relation to sexual vices: The Eugenics Review, **14**, no. 3, 190–193. PMID 21259751

Fisher, R. A., 1999, *The Genetical Theory of Natural Selection*. (1999 variorum edition edited by J. H. Bennett): Oxford University Press (first published 1930).

Fisher, R. A., 1950, *Creative aspects of natural law*. The Eddington Memorial Lecture: Cambridge University Press.

Fisher, R. A., 1951, Limits to intensive production in animals: British Agricultural Bulletin, **4**, 217–218.

Forgash, A. J., 1984, History, evolution and consequences of insecticide resistance: Pesticide Biochemistry and Physiology, **22**, no. 2, 178–186. 10.1016/0048-3575(84)90087-7

Fossøy, F., Moksnes, A., Røskaft, E., Antonov, A., Dyrcz, A., Moskat, C., Ranke, P. S., Rutila, J., Vikan, J. R. and Stokke, B. G. 2012 Sex allocation in relation to host races in the brood-parasitic common cuckoo (Cuculus canorus). PLoS One 7 e36884 1–5.

Foster, K. R., T. Wenseleers, and F. L. W. Ratnieks, 2001, Spite: Hamilton's unproven theory: Annales Zoologici Fennici, **38**, 229–238.

Foth, C., H. Tischlinger, and O. W. M. Rauhut, 2014, New specimen of *Archaeopteryx* provides insights into the evolution of pennaceous feathers: Nature, **511**, no. 7507, 79–82. 10.1038/nature13467 PMID 24990749

Franklin, I. R., 1980, Evolutionary change in small populations, in M. Soule and B. Wilcox, eds., Conservation bi ology: An evolutionary-ecological perspective: Sinauer, 135–149.

Fraser, G. R., 1976 Contributions to round table on Genetic variability of man; Effect of behaviour. Pp. 328–332. In: Galpérine, C, Ed: Proceedings of the International Conference-- Biology and the Future of Man. pp 328–332. Universities of Paris, 1976.

Freeman, R. A., 1921, Social Decay and Regeneration: Houghton Mifflin.

Freud, S., 1956, *Totem und Tabu Einige Übereinstimmungen im Seelenleben der Wilden und der Neurotiker.* Frankfurt a: M., Fischer Taschenbuch Verlag.

Gadagkar, R., 2001, *The Social Biology of* Ropalidia marginata *Toward understanding the evolution of eusociality*: Harvard University Press.

Gagliano, M., and M. Grimonprez, 2015, Breaking the silence – language and the making of meaning in plants: Ecopsychology, **7**, no. 3, 145–152. 10.1089/eco.2015.0023

Ghoul, M., A. S. Griffin, and S. A. West, 2014, Toward an evolutionary definition of cheating: Evolution, **68**, no. 2, 318–331. 10.1111/evo.12266 PMID 24131102

Giraldo, Y. M., J. F. Kamhi, V. Fourcassié, M. Moreau, S. K. A. Robson, A. Rusakov, L. Wimberly, A. Diloreto, A. Kordek, and J. F. A. Traniello, 2016, Lifespan behavioural and neural resilience in a social insect: Proceedings. Biological Sciences, **283**, no. 1822, 20152603. 10.1098/rspb.2015.2603 PMID 26740614

Goethe, J. W. A., 1850, Conversations of Goethe with Eckermann and Soret, **v. 2**. J. Oxenford, trans.: Smith Elder & Co.

Gogarten, J. P., and E. Hilario, 2006, Inteins, introns, and homing endonucleases: recent revelations about the life cycle of parasitic genetic elements: BMC Evolutionary Biology, **6**, no. 1, 94, accessed 15 February 2017. 10.1186/1471-2148-6-94 PMID 17101053

Gómez, J. M., M. Verdú, A. González-Megías, and M. Méndez, 2016, The phylogenetic roots of human lethal violence: Nature, **538**, no. 7624, 233–237, accessed 10 October 2016. 10.1038/nature19758 PMID 27680701

Gould, S. J., 1990, Wonderful Life: The Burgess Shale and the nature of history: Norton.

Gould, S. J., 2002, The Structure of Evolution: Belknap Press.

Green, S., 1981, *Prehistorian: A biography of V. Gordon Childe* Bradford on Avon: Monnraker Press.

Guillot, M., 1948, Anosmies partielles et odeurs fondamentales: Comptes Rendus de l'Academie Sciences, **226**, 1307–1309.

Guo, G., Y. Tong, and T. Cai, 2008, Gene by social context interactions for number of sexual partners among white male youths: genetics-informed sociology: American Journal of Sociology, **114**, no. S1, Suppl, S36–S66. 10.1086/592207 PMID 19569400

Gustavson, D. E., A. Miyake, J. K. Hewitt, and N. P. Friedman, 2014, Genetic relations among procrastination, impulsivity, and goal-management ability: implications for the evolutionary origin of procrastination: Psychological Science, **25**, no. 6, 1178–1188. 10.1177/0956797614526260 PMID 24705635

Guyau, 1885 (reprint from 1903), *Esquisse d'une morale sans obligation ni sanction*, 6th ed.: Ancienne Librairie Germer Baillière.

Hahn, E., J. Gottschling, C. J. König, and F. M. Spinath, 2016, The heritability of job satisfaction reconsidered: only unique environmental influences beyond personality: Journal of Business and Psychology, **31**, no. 2, 217–231. 10.1007/s10869-015-9413-x

Haldane, J. B. S., 1928, Possible Worlds and Other Essays: Chatto and Windus.

Haldane, J. B. S., 1932, *The Inequality of* Man: Penguin Books.

Hall, M., 2011, Plants as Persons A philosophical botany: SUNY Press.

Hamilton, W. D., 1964a, The genetical evolution of social behaviour. I: Journal of Theoretical Biology, **7**, no. 1, 1–16. 10.1016/0022-5193(64)90038-4 PMID 5875341

Hamilton, W. D., 1964b, The genetical evolution of social behaviour. II: Journal of Theoretical Biology, **7**, no. 1, 17–52. 10.1016/0022-5193(64)90039-6 PMID 5875340

Hamilton, W. D., 1970, Selfish and spiteful behaviour in an evolutionary model: Nature, **228**, no. 5277, 1218–1220. 10.1038/2281218a0 PMID 4395095

Handreck, K., 1997, Phosphorus requirements of Australian native plants: Australian Journal of Soil Science, **35**, no. 2, 241–289. 10.1071/S96060

Hanigan, I. C., C. D. Butler, P. N. Kokic, M. F. Hutchinson, and M. F. Hutchinson, 2012, Suicide and drought in New South Wales, Australia, 1970–2007: Proceedings of the National Academy of Sciences of the United States of America, **109**, no. 35, 13950–13955. 10.1073/pnas.1112965109 PMID 22891347

Hansen, S., 2001, Book review: *A Natural History of Rape Biological bases of sexual coercion*: Journal of International Women's Studies, **2**, 104–109.

Harden, L. M., S. Kent, Q. J. Pittman, and J. Roth, 2015, Fever and sickness behavior: Friend or foe?: Brain, Behavior, and Immunity, **50**, 322–333. 10.1016/j.bbi.2015.07.012 PMID 26187566

Hare, R. M., Schlatter, S., Rhodes, G. and Simmons, L. W. 2017 Putative sex-specific human pheromones do not affect gender perception, attractiveness ratings or unfaithfulness judgements of opposite sex faces. R. Soc. open sci. 4: 160831. http://dx.doi.org/10.1098/rsos.160831 (accessed 10 March 2017)

Harris, S., 2010 *The Moral Landscape*. London, Bantam Press. (Citations from 2012 cheap reprint, London, Transworld Publishers)

Haslam, N., and S. Loughnan, 2014, Dehumanization and infrahumanization: Annual Review of Psychology, **65**, no. 1, 399–423. 10.1146/annurev-psych-010213-115045 PMID 23808915

Hasselquist, D., and P. W. Sherman, 2001, Social mating systems and extrapair fertilizations in passerine birds: Behavioural Ecology, **12**, no. 4, 457–466. 10.1093/beheco/12.4.457

Hazlett, H. C., H. Gu, B. C. Munsell, S. H. Kim, M. Styner, J. J. Wolff, J. T. Elison, M. R. Swanson, H. Zhu, K. N. Botteron, D. L. Collins, J. N. Constantino, S. R. Dager, A. M. Estes, A. C. Evans, V. S. Fonov, G. Gerig, P. Kostopoulos, R. C. McKinstry, J. Pandey, S. Paterson, J. R. Pruett, R. T. Schultz, D. W. Shaw, L. Zwaigenbaum, J. Piven, J. Piven, H. C. Hazlett, C. Chappell, S. R. Dager, A. M. Estes, D. W. Shaw, K. N. Botteron, R. C. McKinstry, J. N. Constantino, J. R. PruettJr., R. T. Schultz, S. Paterson, L. Zwaigenbaum, J. T. Elison, J. J. Wolff, A. C. Evans, D. L. Collins, G. B. Pike, V. S. Fonov, P. Kostopoulos, S. Das, G. Gerig, M. Styner, and C. H. Gu, and the IBIS Network, and the Clinical Sites, and the Data Coordinating Center, and the Image Processing Core, and the Statistical Analysis, 2017, Early brain development in infants at high risk for autism spectrum disorder: Nature, **542**, no. 7641, 348–351. 10.1038/nature21369 PMID 28202961

Hintz, M., C. Bartholmes, P. Nutt, J. Ziermann, S. Hameister, B. Neuffer, and G. Theissen, 2006, Catching a 'hopeful monster': shepherd's purse (*Capsella bursa-pastoris*) as a model system to study the evolution of flower development: Journal of Experimental Botany, **57**, no. 13, 3531–3542. 10.1093/jxb/erl158 PMID 17018770

Howard, M. W., and H. Eichenbaum, 2014, Time and space in the hippocampus: Brain Research. 10.1016/j.brainres.2014.10.069 PMID 25449892

Hur, Y.-M., H.-U. Jeong, J. A. Schermer, and J. P. Rushton, 2011, Miserliness is heritable: Personality and Individual Differences, **51**, no. 8, 1052–1055. 10.1016/j.paid.2011.08.005

Huxley, J., 1941, The Uniqueness of Man: Chatto & Windus.

Huxley, L., 1900, Life and Letters of Thomas Henry Huxley, **v. 1**: Macmillan. 10.5962/bhl.title.54282

Huxley, T. H. 1893. Collected Essays. Vol. 1 Methods and Results. London, Macmillan.

Huxley, T. H., 1894a, Man's Place in Nature and other essays: Macmillan.

Huxley, T. H., 1894b, Science and Christian Tradition: Macmillan.

Huxley, T. H., 1894c, Evolution and Ethics: Macmillan.

Huxley, T. H., 1894d, Hume: With helps to the study of Berkeley: Macmillan. 10.1037/12932-000

Höbel, G., 2014, Effect of temporal and spectral noise features on gap detection behavior by calling green treefrogs: Behavioural Processes, **108**, 43–49. 10.1016/j.beproc.2014.09.013 PMID 25242723

Irvine, W., 1959, The influence of Darwin on literature: Proceedings of the American Philosophical Society, **103**, 616–628.

Jarvi, T., E. Roskaft, and T. Slagsvold, 1982, The conflict between male polygamy and female monogamy: some comments on the "cheating hypothesis": American Naturalist, **120**, no. 5, 689–691. 10.1086/284021

Jing, L., Duan, T.-T., Tian, M., Yuan, Q., Tan, J.-W., Zhu, Y.-Y., Ding, Z.-Y., Cao, J., Yang, Y.-X., Zhang, X., Mao, R.-R., Richter-Levin, G., Zhou, Q.-X. & Xu, L.2015 Despair-associated memory requires a slow-onset CA1 long-term potentiation with unique underlying mechanisms. Scientific Reports | 5:15000 | DOI: 10.1038/srep15000 (accessed 12 June 2016)

Johnson, E. A., 2014, Ask the Beasts Darwin and the God of Love: Bloomsbury.

Jordan, J. J., M. Hoffman, P. Bloom, and D. G. Rand, 2016, Third-party punishment as a costly signal of trustworthiness: Nature, **530**, no. 7591, 473–476. 10.1038/nature16981 PMID 26911783

Kaiser-Bunbury, C. N., J. Mougal, A. E. Whittington, T. Valentin, R. Gabriel, J. M. Olesen, and N. Blüthgen, 2017, Ecosystem restoration strengthens pollination network resilience and function: Nature, **542**, no. 7640, 223–227, accessed 31 January 2017. 10.1038/nature21071 PMID 28135718

Karp, N. A., Mason, J., Beaudet, A. L., Benjamini, Y., Bower, L., Braun, R. E., Brown, S. D. M., Chesler, E. J., Dickinson, M. E., Flenniken, A. M., Fuchs, H., Hrabe de Angelis, M., XiangGao, X., Guo, S., Greenaway, S., Heller, R., Herault, Y., Justice, M. J., Kurbatova, N., Lelliott, C. J., K. C. Kent Lloyd, K. C. K., Mallon, A.-M., Mank, J. E., Masuya, H., McKerlie, C., Meehan, T. F., Mott, R. F., Murray, S. A., Parkinson, H., Ramirez-Solis, R., Santos, L., Seavitt, J. R., Smedley, D., Sorg, T., Speak, A. O., Steel, K. P., Svenson, K. L., The International Mouse Phenotyping Consortium, Wakana, S., West, D., Wells, S., Westerberg, H., Yaacoby, S. and White, J. K. 2017 Prevalence of sexual dimorphism in mammalian phenotypic traits. Nature Communications | 8:15475 | DOI: 10.1038/ncomms15475 | (accessed 29 June 2017).

Keller, L., 2009, Adaptation and the genetics of social behaviour: Philosophical Transactions of the Royal Society of London. Series B, Biological Sciences, **364**, no. 1533, 3209–3216, accessed 2 October 2016. 10.1098/rstb.2009.0108 PMID 19805428

Kendler, K. S., M. Gatz, C. O. Gardner, and N. L. Pedersen, 2006, A Swedish national twin study of lifetime major depression: The American Journal of Psychiatry, **163**, no. 1, 109–114. 10.1176/appi.ajp.163.1.109 PMID 16390897

Keynes, J. M., 1946, Newton, the man, pp. 27–34 in The Royal Society tercentenary celebrations 15–19 July 1946 (Cambridge: CUP, 1947).

Kipling, R. 1910 *Rewards and Fairies*.

Kitcher, P., 2007, Living with Darwin Evolution, design and the future of faith: Oxford University Press.

Kong, A., M. L. Frigge, G. Thorleifsson, H. Stefansson, A. I. Young, F. Zink, G. A. Jonsdottir, A. Okbay, P. Sulem, G. Masson, D. F. Gudbjartsson, A. Helgason, G. Bjornsdottir, U. Thorsteinsdottir, and K. Stefansson, 2017, Selection against variants in the genome associated with educational attainment: Proceedings of the National Academy of Sciences of the United States of America, **114**, no. 5, E727–E732, accessed 2 February 2017. 10.1073/pnas.1612113114 PMID 28096410

Kontis, V., J. E. Bennett, C. D. Mathers, G. Li, K. Foreman, and M. Ezzati, 2017, Future life expectancy in 35 industrialised countries: projections with a Bayesian model ensemble: Lancet, **389**, no. 10076, 1323–1335, accessed 27 February 2017. 10.1016/S0140-6736(16)32381-9 PMID 28236464

Kornhuber, H. H., and L. Deecke, 1965, Hirnpotentialänderungen bei Willkürbewegungen und passiven Bewegungen des Menschen: Bereitschaftspotential und reafferente Potentiale: Pflügers Archiv für die Gesamte Physiologie des Menschen und der Tiere, **284**, no. 1, 1–17, accessed 24 April 2017. 10.1007/BF00412364 PMID 14341490

Kotyk, M. and Varadínová, Z. 2017 Wing reduction influences male mating success but not female fitness in cockroaches. Scientific Reports |7:2367 | DOI:10.1038/s41598-017-02647-7 (accessed 13 June 2017)

Kvon, E. Z., O. K. Kamneva, U. S. Melo, I. Barozzi, M. Osterwalder, B. J. Mannion, V. Tissières, C. S. Pickle, I. Plajzer-Frick, E. A. Lee, M. Kato, T. H. Garvin, J. A. Akiyama, V. Afzal, J. Lopez-Rios, E. M. Rubin, D. E. Dickel, L. A. Pennacchio, and A. Visel, 2016, Progressive loss of function in a limb enhancer during snake evolution: Cell, **167**, no. 3, 633–642.e11. 10.1016/j.cell.2016.09.028 PMID 27768887

Lai, C. S. L., S. E. Fisher, J. A. Hurst, F. Vargha-Khadem, and A. P. Monaco, 2001, A forkhead-domain gene is mutated in a severe speech and language disorder: Nature, **413**, no. 6855, 519–523. 10.1038/35097076 PMID 11586359

Lankester, E. R., 1907, The Kingdom of Man: Constable. 10.5962/bhl.title.23403

Laski, H. J., 1944, Faith, Reason and Civilisation An essay in historical analysis: Gollancz.

Lawson, D. W., and M. Borgerhoff Mulder, 2016, The offspring quantity-quality trade-off and human fertility variation: Philosophical Transactions of the Royal Society of London. Series B, Biological Sciences, **371**, no. 1692, 20150145, accessed 9 June 2017. 10.1098/rstb.2015.0145 PMID 27022072

Leal, F., and M. J. Cohn, 2016, Loss and re-emergence of legs in snakes by modular evolution of *Sonic hedgehog* and *HOXD* enhancers: Current Biology, **26**, no. 21, 2966–2973. 10.1016/j.cub.2016.09.020 PMID 27773569

Lesch, M., and W. L. Nyhan, 1964, A familial disorder of uric acid metabolism and central nervous system function: The American Journal of Medicine, **36**, no. 4, 561–570. 10.1016/0002-9343(64)90104-4 PMID 14142409

Letenneur, L., 2004, Risk of dementia and alcohol and wine consumption: a review of recent results: Biological Research, **37**, no. 2, 189–193. 10.4067/S0716-97602004000200003 PMID 15455646

Levit, G. S., K. Meister, and U. Hossfeld, 2008, Alternative evolutionary theories: an historical survey: Journal of Bioeconomics, **10**, no. 1, 71–96. 10.1007/s10818-008-9032-y

Lewontin, R. C., 1969, The bases of conflict in biological explanation: Journal of the History of Biology, **2**, no. 1, 34–45. 10.1007/BF00137266

Li, Z., Mingh, Z., Abdalla, B. A., Zhang, Z., Xu, Z., Ye, Q., XU, H., Luo, W., Nie, Q. and Zhang, X. 2016 Genome-wide study of aggression in chicken. Scientific Reports |6:30981|DOI:10.1038/srep30981 (accessed 31 October 2016)

Libet, B., C. A. Gleason, E. W. Wright, and D. K. Pearl, 1983, Time of conscious intention to act in relation to onset of cerebral activity (readiness-potential). The unconscious initiation of a freely voluntary act: Brain, **106**, no. Pt 3, 623–642. 10.1093/brain/106.3.623 PMID 6640273

Logan, D. W., 2015, The complexity of pheromone-mediated behaviour in mammals: Current Opinion in Behavioral Sciences, **2**, 96–101. 10.1016/j.cobeha.2014.10.011

Lorenz, K., 1965a, So kam der Mensch auf den Hund: Deutsche Taschenbuch Verlag.

Lorenz, K., 1965b, Evolution and Modification of Behaviour: University of Chicago Press.

Lozupone, C. A., J. I. Stombaugh, J. I. Gordon, J. K. Jansson, and R. Knight, 2012, Diversity, stability and resilience of the human gut microbiota: Nature, **489**, no. 7415, 220–230. 10.1038/nature11550 PMID 22972295

Lu, H., Yang, P., Xu, Y., Luo, L., Zhu, J., Cui, N., Kang, L. and Cui, F. 2016 Performances of survival, feeding behavior, and gene expression in aphids reveal their different fitness to host alteration. Scientific Reports | 6:19344 | DOI: 10.1038/srep19344 accessed 20 January 2016.

MacColl, A. D. C., and B. J. Hatchwell, 2003, Heritability of parental effort in a passerine bird: Evolution; International Journal of Organic Evolution, **57**, no. 9, 2191–2195. 10.1111/j.0014-3820.2003.tb00398.x PMID 14575340

Macdonell, A. A., 1924, Immortality in Indian thought, in J. Marchant, ed., Immortality: Putnam, 39–58.

Makower, S. V., and B. H. Blackwell, eds., 1912, A book of English essays (1600–1900): Oxford University Press.

Maley, W., 2016, *What* is *a Refugee?*: Scribe.

Malthus, T., 1798. An Essay on the Principle of Population and other writings. (Ed. R Mayhew, 2015) London, Penguin.

Martin, N. G., L. J. Eaves, A. C. Heath, R. Jardine, L. M. Feingold, and H. J. Eysenck, 1986, Transmission of social attitudes: Proceedings of the National Academy of Sciences of the United States of America, **83**, no. 12, 4364–4368. 10.1073/pnas.83.12.4364 PMID 3459179

Maruyama, M., and J. Parker, 2017, Deep-time convergence in rove beetle symbionts of army ants: Current Biology, **27**, no. 6, 920–926. 10.1016/j.cub.2017.02.030 PMID 28285995

Mason, D. A., and P. J. Frick, 1994, The heritability of antisocial behaviour: a meta-analysis of twin and adoption studies: Journal of Psychopathology and Behavioral Assessment, **16**, no. 4, 301–323. 10.1007/BF02239409

Mayo, O., 1972, Fundamental and population genetics, pp. 3–65 in Textbook of Human Genetics (Eds. G. R. Fraser & O. Mayo): Oxford, Blackwell Scientific.

Mayo, O., 1983, Natural Selection and its Constraints: Academic Press.

Mayo, O., 1987, The Theory of Plant Breeding, 2nd ed.: Oxford University Press.

Mayo, O., 2011, Interaction between genotype and environment: a tale of two concepts: Transactions of the Royal Society of South Australia, **135**, no. 2, 113–123. 10.1080/03721426.2011.10887151

Mayo, O., and C. R. Leach, 1985, Models of parent-offspring conflict in small populations: Biometrical Journal. Biometrische Zeitschrift, **5**, no. 5, 483–489. 10.1002/bimj.4710270502

Mayo, O., R. Bürger, and C. R. Leach, 1990, The heritability of fitness: some single gene models: Theoretical and Applied Genetics, **79**, no. 2, 278–284. 10.1007/BF00225964 PMID 24226231

Mayo, O., M. M. Nelson, and J. O. Forfar, 1973, Variation in human fertility: Human Heredity, **23**, no. 5, 401–413. 10.1159/000152605 PMID 4785871

Mayr, E., 1991, One Long Argument Charles Darwin and the Genesis of Modern Evolutionary Thought: Harvard University Press.

McAuliffe, K., P. R. Blake, N. Steinbeis, and F. Warneken, 2017 The developmental foundations of human fairness. Nature Human Behaviour 1, 0042 (2017) | DOI: 10.1038/s41562-016-0042 | www.nature.com/nathumbehav (accessed 23 February 2017)

McCann, K. S., 2000, The diversity-stability debate: Nature, **405**, no. 6783, 228–233. 10.1038/35012234 PMID 10821283

McGuire, S., and J. Clifford, 2000, Genetic and environmental contributions to loneliness in children: Psychological Science, **11**, no. 6, 487–491. 10.1111/1467-9280.00293 PMID 11202494

McKenzie, J. A., and A. Y. Game, 1987, Diazinon resistance in *Lucilia cuprina*; mapping of a fitness modifier: Heredity, **59**, no. 3, 371–381. 10.1038/hdy.1987.145

Medawar, P. B., 1946, Old age and natural death: Modern Quarterly, **2**, 30–49.

Mednick, S. A., and K. M. Finello, 1983, Biological factors and crime: implications for forensic psychiatry: International Journal of Law and Psychiatry, **6**, no. 1, 1–15. 10.1016/0160-2527(83)90003-1 PMID 6642820

Mellander, S., P.-O. Andersson, L.-E. Afzelius, and P. Hellstrand, 1982, Neural beta-adrenergic dilatation of the facial vein in man. Possible mechanism in emotional blushing: Acta Physiologica Scandinavica, **114**, no. 3, 393–399. 10.1111/j.1748-1716.1982.tb07000.x PMID 6291328

Méndez-Bértolo, C., S. Moratti, R. Toledano, F. Lopez-Sosa, R. Martínez-Alvarez, Y. H. Mah, P. Vuilleumier, A. Gil-Nagel, and B. A. Strange, 2016, A fast pathway for fear in human amygdala: Nature Neuroscience, **19**, no. 8, 1041–1049. 10.1038/nn.4324 PMID 27294508

Mischkowski, D. & Glöckner, A. 2016 Spontaneous cooperation for prosocials, but not for proselfs: Social value orientation moderates spontaneous cooperation behaviour. Scientific Reports | 6:21555 | DOI: 10.1038/srep21555 (accessed 17 February 2016.)

Monti, M. M., E. S. Lutkenhoff, M. Rubinov, P. Boveroux, A. Vanhaudenhuyse, O. Gosseries, M.-A. Bruno, Q. Noirhomme, M. Boly, and S. Laureys, 2013, Dynamic change of global and local information processing in propofol-induced loss and recovery of consciousness: PLoS Computational Biology, **9**, no. 10, e1003271, accessed 26 August 2016. 10.1371/journal.pcbi.1003271 PMID 24146606

Newman, D., and D. Pilson, 1997, Increased probability of extinction due to decreased genetic effective population size: Evolution; International Journal of Organic Evolution, **51**, no. 2, 354–362. 10.1111/j.1558-5646.1997.tb02422.x PMID 28565367

Nguyen, T. B., J. M. Gunn, M. Potiriadis, I. P. Everall, and C. A. Bousman, 2015, Serotonin transporter polymorphism (5HTTLPR), severe childhood abuse and depressive symptom trajectories in adulthood: British Journal of Psychology Open, **1**, no. 1, 104–109. 10.1192/bjpo.bp.115.000380 PMID 27703731

Nicholls, N., C. D. Butler, and I. Hanigan, 2006, Inter-annual rainfall variations and suicide in New South Wales, Australia, 1964–2001: International Journal of Biometeorology, **50**, no. 3, 139–143. 10.1007/s00484-005-0002-y PMID 16235091

Noble, D., 2006, The Music of Life Biology beyond genes: Oxford University Press.

Nowack, J., Rojas, A. D., Ko[Umlaut]ntner, G. And Geiser, F. 2015 Snoozing through the storm: torpor use during a natural disaster. Scientific Reports 5 doi:10.1038|srep11243. (Accessed 2 November 2016)

Okbay, A., B. M. L. Baselmans, J. E. De Neve, P. Turley, M. G. Nivard, M. A. Fontana, S. F. W. Meddens, R. K. Linnér, C. A. Rietveld, J. Derringer, J. Gratten, J. J. Lee, J. Z. Liu, R.de Vlaming, T. S. Ahluwalia, J. Buchwald, A. Cavadino, A. C. Frazier-Wood, N. A. Furlotte, V. Garfield, M. H. Geisel, J. R. Gonzalez, S. Haitjema, R. Karlsson, S. W.van der Laan, K.-H. Ladwig, J. Lahti, S. J.van der Lee, P. A. Lind, T. Liu, L. Matteson, E. Mihailov, M. B. Miller, C. C. Minica, I. M. Nolte, D. Mook-Kanamori, P. J.van der Most, C. Oldmeadow, Y. Qian, O. Raitakari, R. Rawal, A. Realo, R. Rueedi, B. Schmidt, A. V. Smith, E. Stergiakouli, T. Tanaka, K. Taylor, J. Wedenoja, J. Wellmann, H.-J. Westra, S. M. Willems, W. Zhao, N. Amin, A. Bakshi, P. A. Boyle, S. Cherney, S. R. Cox, G. Davies, O. S. Davis, J. Ding, N. Direk, P. Eibich, R. T. Emeny, G. Fatemifar, J. D. Faul, L. Ferrucci, A. Forstner, C. Gieger, R. Gupta, T. B. Harris, J. M. Harris, E. G. Holliday, J. J. Hottenga, P. L. De Jager, M. A. Kaakinen, E. Kajantie, V. Karhunen, I. Kolcic, M. Kumari, L. J. Launer, L. Franke, R. Li-Gao, M. Koini, A. Loukola, P. Marques-Vidal, G. W. Montgomery, M. A. Mosing, L. Paternoster, A. Pattie, K. E. Petrovic, L. Pulkki-Råback, L. Quaye, K. Räikkönen, I. Rudan, R. J. Scott, J. A. Smith, A. R. Sutin, M. Trzaskowski, A. E. Vinkhuyzen, L. Yu, D. Zabaneh, J. R. Attia, D. A. Bennett, K. Berger, L. Bertram, D. I. Boomsma, H. Snieder, S. C. Chang, F. Cucca, I. J. Deary, C. M.van Duijn, J. G. Eriksson, U. Bültmann, E. J.de Geus, P. J. Groenen, V. Gudnason, T. Hansen, C. A. Hartman, C. M. Haworth, C. Hayward, A. C. Heath, D. A. Hinds, E. Hyppönen, W. G. Iacono, M. R. Järvelin, K. H. Jöckel, J. Kaprio, S. L. Kardia, L. Keltikangas-Järvinen, P. Kraft, L. D. Kubzansky, T. Lehtimäki, P. K. Magnusson, N. G. Martin, M. McGue, A. Metspalu, M. Mills, R.de Mutsert, A. J. Oldehinkel, G. Pasterkamp, N. L. Pedersen, R. Plomin, O. Polasek, C. Power, S. S. Rich, F. R. Rosendaal, H. M.den Ruijter, D. Schlessinger, H. Schmidt, R. Svento, R. Schmidt, B. Z. Alizadeh, T. I. Sørensen, T. D. Spector, A. Steptoe, A. Terracciano, A. R. Thurik, N. J. Timpson, H. Tiemeier, A. G. Uitterlinden, P. Vollenweider, G. G. Wagner, D. R. Weir, J. Yang, D. C. Conley, G. D. Smith, A. Hofman, M. Johannesson, D. I. Laibson, S. E. Medland, M. N. Meyer, J. K. Pickrell, T. Esko, R. F. Krueger, J. P. Beauchamp, P. D. Koellinger, D. J. Benjamin, M. Bartels, and D. Cesarini, and the LifeLines Cohort Study, 2016, Genetic variants associated with subjective well-being, depressive symptoms, and neuroticism identified through genome-wide analyses: Nature Genetics, **48**, no. 6, 624–633. 10.1038/ng.3552 PMID 27089181

Park, M., J. E. Verhoeven, P. Cuijpers, C. F. ReynoldsIII, and B. W. J. H. Penninx, 2015, Where you live may make you old: the association between perceived poor neighborhood quality and leukocyte telomere length: PLoS One, **10**, no. 6, e0128460, accessed 14 June 2017. 10.1371/journal.pone.0128460 PMID 26083263

Parrott, W. G., and R. H. Smith, 1993, Distinguishing the experiences of envy and jealousy: Journal of Personality and Social Psychology, **64**, no. 6, 906–920. 10.1037/0022-3514.64.6.906 PMID 8326472

Partinen, M., J. Kaprio, M. Koskenvuo, P. Putkonen, and H. Langinvainio, 1983, Genetic and environmental determination of human sleep: Sleep, **6**, no. 3, 179–185. 10.1093/sleep/6.3.179 PMID 6684786

Paul, Jean [Jean Paul Friedrich Richter] 1809 Dr Katzenbergers Badereise. 1960 edition. München, Wilhelm Goldmann Verlag.

Penrose, R., 1989, The Emperor's New Mind: Concerning computers, minds and the laws of physics: Oxford University Press.

Plomin, R., 1986, Development, genetics, and psychology: Erlbaum.

Polderman, T. J. C., B. Benyamin, C. A.de Leeuw, P. F. Sullivan, A.van Bochoven, P. M. Visscher, and D. Posthuma, 2015, Meta-analysis of the heritability of human traits based on fifty years of twin studies: Nature Genetics, **47**, no. 7, 702–709. 10.1038/ng.3285 PMID 25985137

Politzer, G., 1947, Le Bergsonisme. Une mystification philosophique: Editions Sociales.

Price, G. R., 1970, Selection and covariance: Nature, **227**, no. 5257, 520–521. 10.1038/227520a0 PMID 5428476

Pruitt, J. N., and J. J. Krauel, 2010, The adaptive value of gluttony: predators mediate the life history trade-offs of satiation threshold: Journal of Evolutionary Biology, **23**, no. 10, 2104–2111. 10.1111/j.1420-9101.2010.02070.x PMID 20840307

Rand, D. G. 2016 Cooperation, fast and slow: meta-analytic evidence for a theory of social heuristics and self-interested deliberation. Psychological Science OnlineFirst 1–15 doi:10.1177/0956797616654455 (accessed 1 August 2016)

Rao, G.-Y., S. Andersson, and B. Widén, 2002, Flower and cotyledon asymmetry in *Brassica cretica*: genetic variation and relationships with fitness: Evolution; International Journal of Organic Evolution, **56**, no. 4, 690–698. 10.1111/j.0014-3820.2002.tb01380.x PMID 12038527

Rao, P. S. S. S., S. G. Inbaraj, and G. Jesudian, 1972, Rural-urban differentials in consanguinity: Journal of Medical Genetics, **9**, no. 2, 174–178. 10.1136/jmg.9.2.174 PMID 5046628

Rai, R., and L. Regan, 2006, Recurrent miscarriage: Lancet, **368**, no. 9535, 601–611. 10.1016/S0140-6736(06)69204-0 PMID 16905025

Rebollo, I., and D. I. Boomsma, 2006, Genetic analysis of anger: genetic dominance or competitive sibling interaction: Behavior Genetics, **36**, no. 2, 216–228. 10.1007/s10519-005-9025-8 PMID 16402285

Rendel, J. M., 1967 *Canalisation and Gene Control*. London, Logos Press (academic Press).

Revelle, W., 1995, Personality processes: Annual Review of Psychology, **46**, no. 1, 295–328. 10.1146/annurev.ps.46.020195.001455

Riddington, R., and A. Gosler, 1995, Differences in reproductive success and parental quality between habitats in the Great Tit *Parus major*: The Ibis, **137**, no. 3, 371–378. 10.1111/j.1474-919X.1995.tb08035.x

Robinson, M., 2010, Absence of Mind the dispelling of inwardness from the modern myth of the self: Yale University Press.

Robinson, M. R., Kleinman, A., Graff, M., VinkhuyzenA. A. E., Couper, D., Miller, M. B., Peyrot, W. J., Abdellaoui, A., Zietsch, B. P., Nolte, I. M., van Vliet-Ostaptchouk, J. V., Snieder, H., The LifeLines Cohort Study, Genetic Investigation of Anthropometric Traits (GIANT) consortium, Medland, S. E., Martin, N. G., Magnusson, P. K. E., Iacono, W. G., McGue, M, North, K. E., Yang, J., and Visscher, P. M. 2017 Genetic evidence of assortative mating in humans. Nature Human Behaviour 1 16–28. | DOI: 10.1038/s41562-016-0016.

Rodgers, J. L., D. C. Rowe, and M. Buster, 1999, Nature, nurture and first sexual intercourse in the USA: fitting behavioural genetic models to NLSY kinship data: Journal of Biosocial Science, **31**, no. 1, 29–41. 10.1017/S0021932099000292 PMID 10081235

Roff, D. A., 1994, Habitat persistence and the evolution of wing dimorphism in insects: American Naturalist, **144**, no. 5, 772–798. 10.1086/285706

Rønning, B., H. Jensen, B. Moe, and C. Bech, 2007, Basal metabolic rate: heritability and genetic correlations with morphological traits in the zebra finch: Journal of Evolutionary Biology, **20**, no. 5, 1815–1822. 10.1111/j.1420-9101.2007.01384.x PMID 17714299

Rost, S., A. Fregin, V. Ivaskevicius, E. Conzelmann, K. Hörtnagel, H.-J. Pelz, K. Lappegard, E. Seifried, I. Scharrer, E. G. D. Tuddenham, C. R. Müller, T. M. Strom, and J. Oldenburg, 2004, Mutations in *VKORC1* cause warfarin resistance and multiple coagulation factor deficiency type 2: Nature, **427**, no. 6974, 537–541. 10.1038/nature02214 PMID 14765194

Rouse, G. W., S. K. Goffredi, and R. C. Vrijenhoek, 2004, *Osedax*: bone-eating marine worms with dwarf males: Science, **305**, no. 5684, 668–671. 10.1126/science.1098650 PMID 15286372

Roy, A., N. L. Segal, B. S. Centerwall, and C. D. Robinette, 1991, Suicide in twins: Archives of General Psychiatry, **48**, no. 1, 29–32. 10.1001/archpsyc.1991.01810250031003 PMID 1984759

Roy, M.-A., M. C. Neale, and K. S. Kendler, 1995, The genetic epidemiology of self-esteem: The British Journal of Psychiatry, **166**, no. 6, 813–820. 10.1192/bjp.166.6.813 PMID 7663835

Rozzi, R., 1999, The reciprocal links between evolutionary-ecological sciences and environmental ethics: Biosciences, **49**, no. 11, 911–921. 10.2307/1313650

Rushton, J. P., D. W. Fulker, M. C. Neale, D. K. B. Nias, and H. J. Eysenck, 1986, Altruism and aggression: the heritability of individual differences: Journal of Personality and Social Psychology, **50**, no. 6, 1192–1198. 10.1037/0022-3514.50.6.1192 PMID 3723334

Ruskin, J. 1860 Essay iii, s54. Unto this last. Four Essays on Political Economy. London (reference from 1903 edition, London, George Allen).

Sachs, J. L., U. G. Mueller, T. P. Wilcox, and J. J. Bull, 2004, The evolution of cooperation: The Quarterly Review of Biology, **79**, no. 2, 135–160. 10.1086/383541 PMID 15232949

Salazar, A., B. Fürstenau, C. Quero, N. Pérez-Hidalgo, P. Carazo, E. Font, and D. Martín-ez-Torres, 2015, Aggressive mimicry coexists with mutualism in an aphid: Proceedings of the

National Academy of Sciences of the United States of America, **112**, no. 4, 1101–1106. 10.1073/pnas.1414061112 PMID 25583474

Sadowska, E. T., M. K. Labocha, K. Baliga, A. Stanisz, A. K. Wróblewska, W. Jagusiak, and P. Koteja, 2005, Genetic correlations between basal and maximum metabolic rates in a wild rodent: consequences for evolution of endothermy: Evolution; International Journal of Organic Evolution, **59**, no. 3, 672–681. 10.1111/j.0014-3820.2005.tb01025.x PMID 15856708

Samas, P., M. E. Hauber, P. Cassey, and T. Grim, 2014, Host responses to interspecific brood parasitism: a by-product of adaptations to conspecific parasitism?: Frontiers in Zoology, **11**, no. 1, 34–45. 10.1186/1742-9994-11-34 PMID 24834103

Hassan, S., and U. Mathesius, 2012, The role of flavonoids in root-rhizosphere signalling: opportunities and challenges for improving plant-microbe interactions: Journal of Experimental Botany, **63**, no. 9, 3429–3444. 10.1093/jxb/err430 PMID 22213816

Savulescu, J., and R. ter Meulen, And Kahane, G. 2011 Enhancing Human Capacities. London, Wiley-Blackwell.

Scarpino, S. V., A. Allard, and L. Hébert-Dufresne, 2016, The effect of a prudent adaptive behaviour on disease transmission: Nature Physics, **12**, no. 11, 1042–1046, accessed 9 August 2016. 10.1038/NPHYS832 10.1038/nphys3832

Schiestl, F. P., 2005, On the success of a swindle: pollination by deception in orchids: Naturwissenschaften, **92**, no. 6, 255–264. 10.1007/s00114-005-0636-y PMID 15931514

Schmidt, K., P. J. Cowen, C. J. Harmer, G. Tzortzis, S. Errington, and P. W. J. Burnet, 2015, Prebiotic intake reduces the waking cortisol response and alters emotional bias in healthy volunteers: Psychopharmacology, **232**, no. 10, 1793–1801. 10.1007/s00213-014-3810-0 PMID 25449699

Sehgal, A., and E. Mignot, 2011, Genetics of sleep and sleep disorders: Cell, **146**, no. 2, 194–207, accessed 19 June 2017. 10.1016/j.cell.2011.07.004 PMID 21784243

Scoville, W. B., and B. Milner, 1957, Loss of recent memory after bilateral hippocampal lesions: Journal of Neurology, Neurosurgery, and Psychiatry, **20**, no. 1, 11–21. 10.1136/jnnp.20.1.11 PMID 13406589

Seckbach J., and R. Gordon, eds., 2008, Divine Action and Natural Selection Science, Faith and Evolution: World Scientific Publishing Co. 10.1142/6998

Segal, N. L., S. M. Wilson, T. J. BouchardJr., and D. G. Gitlin, 1995, Comparative grief experiences of bereaved twins and other bereaved relatives: Personality and Individual Differences, **18**, no. 4, 511–524. 10.1016/0191-8869(94)00174-Q

Sheng, Y., Zhao, W., Song, Y., Li, Z., Luo, M., Lei, Q., Cheng, H. & Zhou, R. 2015 Proteomic analysis of three gonad types of swamp eel reveals genes differentially expressed during sex reversal. Scientific Reports | 5:10176 | DOI: 10.1038/srep10176

Shurts, S. E., 2013, Resentment and the right: a twentieth-century cycle of reaction, revaluation, and retreat by the French extreme right: European History Quarterly, **43**, no. 2, 257–278. 10.1177/0265691413478543

Simon, H. A., 1956, Rational choice and the structure of the environment: Psychological Review, **63**, no. 2, 129–138. 10.1037/h0042769 PMID 13310708

Skinner, B. F., 1971, Beyond Freedom and Dignity: Penguin Books [later edition].

Slotkin, T. A., A. Stadler, S. Skavicus, J. Card, J. Ruff, E. D. Levin, and F. J. Seidler, 2017, Is There a critical period for the developmental neurotoxicity of low-level tobacco smoke exposure?: Toxicological Sciences, **155**, no. 1, 75–84. 10.1093/toxsci/kfw180 PMID 27633979

Smith, C., 1975, Quantitative inheritance, in G. R. Fraser and O. Mayo, eds., Textbook of Human Genetics: Blackwell, 382–441.

Smith, J. M., 1968, Mathematical Ideas in Biology: Cambridge University Press. 10.1017/CBO9780511565144

Soler, J. J., M. Soler, T. Pérez-Contreras, S. Aragón, and A. P. Møller, 1999, Antagonistic antiparasite defences: nest defence and egg rejection in the magpie host of the great spotted cuckoo: Behavioral Ecology, **10**, no. 6, 707–713. 10.1093/beheco/10.6.707

Speed, D., and D. J. Balding, 2015, Relatedness in the post-genomic era: is it still useful?: Nature Reviews. Genetics, **16**, no. 1, 33–44. 10.1038/nrg3821 PMID 25404112

Stuart, V., and D. W. Klumpp, 1984, Evidence for food-resource partitioning by kelp-bed filter: Marine Ecology Progress Series, **16**, 27–37. 10.3354/meps016027

Subramaniam, B., 2014, Ghost Stories for Darwin the science of variation and the politics of diversity: University of Illinois Press.

Sudo, R. and Tsukamoto, K. 2015 Migratory restlessness and the role of androgen for increasing behavioural drive in the spawning migration of the Japanese eel. Scientific Reports | 5:17430 | DOI: 10.1038/srep17430 (accessed 26 June 2016)

Thoday, J. M., 1958, Natural selection and biological progress, in S. A. Barnett, ed., A Century of Darwin: Heinemann, 313–333.

Thornhill, R., and C. T. Palmer, 2000, A Natural History of Rape Biological bases of sexual coercion: MIT.

Tirandaz, A., Ghahramani, F. T. And Salari, V. 2017. Validity examination of the dissipative quantum model of olfaction. Scientific Reports | 7:4432 | DOI: 10.1038/s41598-017-04846-8 (accessed 15 July 2016)

Tremblay, R. E., 2010, Developmental origins of disruptive behaviour problems: the 'original sin' hypothesis, epigenetics and their consequences for prevention: Journal of Child Psychology and Psychiatry, and Allied Disciplines, **51**, no. 4, 341–367. 10.1111/j.1469-7610.2010.02211.x PMID 20146751

Tsujino, M., and T. H. Takahashi, 2012, Natural genetic variation in fluctuating asymmetry of wing shape in *Drosophila melanogaster*: Ecological Research, **27**, no. 1, 133–143. 10.1007/s11284-011-0880-x

Tuvblad, C., and L. A. Baker, 2011, Human aggression across the lifespan: genetic propensities and environmental moderators: Advances in Genetics, **75**, 171–214. 10.1016/B978-0-12-380858-5.00007-1 PMID 22078481

Van Cauwenberghe, C., C. Van Broeckhoven, and K. Sleegers, 2016, The genetic landscape of Alzheimer disease: clinical implications and perspectives: Genetics in Medicine, **18**, no. 5, 421–430. 10.1038/gim.2015.117 PMID 26312828

Veroude, K., Y. Zhang-James, N. Fernàndez-Castillo, M. J. Bakker, B. Cormand, and S. V. Faraone, 2016, Genetics of aggressive behavior: An overview: American Journal of Medical Genetics B, **171B**, no. 1, 3–43. 10.1002/ajmg.b.32364 PMID 26345359

Vining, D. R., 1986, Social versus reproductive success: the central theoretical problem of human sociobiology: Behavioral and Brain Sciences, **9**, no. 01, 167–216. 10.1017/S0140525X00021968

Voracek, M., and L. M. Loibl, 2007, Genetics of suicide: a systematic review of twin studies: Wiener Klinische Wochenschrift, **119**, no. 15–16, 463–475. 10.1007/s00508-007-0823-2 PMID 17721766

Waddington, C. H., 1941, The Scientific Attitude: Penguin Books.

Waddington, C. H., 1957, The strategy of the genes: A discussion of some aspects of theoretical biology: Allen & Unwin.

Wardle, J., and S. Carnell, 2009, Appetite is a heritable phenotype associated with adiposity: Annals of Behavioral Medicine, **38**, no. S1, Suppl 1, S25–S30. 10.1007/s12160-009-9116-5 PMID 19730964

Watson, P., 2011, The German Genius Europe's Third Renaissance, the Second Scientific Revolution and the Twentieth Century: Simon & Schuster.

Wei, D., D.-Y. Lee, C. D. Cox, C. A. Karsten, O. Peñagarikano, D. H. Geschwind, C. H. Gall, and C. Piomelli, 2015 Endocannabinoid signaling mediates oxytocin-driven social reward. PNAS www.pnas.org/cgi/content/short/1509795112 (accessed 24 November 2015). 10.1073/pnas.1509795112

Whitehead, A. N., 1926/1938, Science and the Modern World, 1938 edition: Penguin Books.

Wolfthal, D., 2001, A Natural History of Rape: Biological Bases of Sexual Coercion (review): Journal of the History of Sexuality, **10**, no. 2, 343–346. 10.1353/sex.2001.0043

World Health Organisation 2015 Suicide rates, age-standardized. Data by country http://apps.who.int/gho/data/node.main.MHSUICIDEASDR?lang=en (accessed 29 June 2017)

Yancey, J. R., N. C. Venables, B. M. Hicks, and C. J. Patrick, 2013, Evidence for a heritable brain basis to deviance-promoting deficits in self-control: Journal of Criminal Justice, **41**, no. 5, 309–317. 10.1016/j.jcrimjus.2013.06.002 PMID 24187392

Yang, Q., Wang, X., Yin, S., Zhao, X., Tan, J. & Chen, A. 2016 Improved emotional conflict control triggered by the processing priority of negative emotion. Scientific Reports | 6:24302 | DOI: 10.1038/srep24302 (accessed 21 April 2016)

Yano, J. M., K. Yu, G. P. Donaldson, G. G. Shastri, P. Ann, L. Ma, C. R. Nagler, R. F. Ismagilov, S. K. Mazmanian, and E. Y. Hsiao, 2015, Indigenous bacteria from the gut microbiota regulate host serotonin biosynthesis: Cell, **161**, no. 2, 264–276. 10.1016/j.cell.2015.02.047 PMID 25860609

Yong, M. H., and T. Ruffman, 2014, Emotional contagion: dogs and humans show a similar physiological response to human infant crying: Behavioural Processes, **108**, 155–165. 10.1016/j.beproc.2014.10.006 PMID 25452080

Yoshimura, C. G., 2010, The experience and communication of envy among siblings, siblings-in-law and spouses: Journal of Social and Personal Relationships, **27**, no. 8, 1075–1088. 10.1177/0265407510382244

Zaidi, A. A., B. C. Mattern, P. Claes, B. McEcoy, C. Hughes, and M. D. Shriver, 2017, Investigating the case of human nose shape and climate adaptation: PLOS Genetics, **13**, no. 3, e1006616, accessed 23 March 2017. 10.1371/journal.pgen.1006616 PMID 28301464

Index

Regina Oehler, Petra Gehring, Volker Mosbrugger (Hrsg.)

BIOLOGIE UND ETHIK: LEBEN ALS PROJEKT

Ein Funkkolleg-Lesebuch mit Provokationen und Denkanstößen

SENCKENBERG

Biologie und Ethik: Leben als Projekt

Hrsg.: Regina Oehler; Petra Gehring; Volker Mosbrugger

2017. 248 Seiten, 14 x 20 cm, (Senckenberg Bücher, Nr. 78)
ISBN 978-3-510-61409-7, brosch., 15.90 €

Mehr Informationen zum Buch:
www.schweizerbart.de/9783510614097

Woher kommen wir Menschen, was sind unsere biologischen Wurzeln? Und wohin gehen wir? Nehmen wir unsere Biologie jetzt selbst in die Hand – wenn wir zum Beispiel mit Genscheren tief ins Erbgut eingreifen? Was machen wir mit der Natur? Woher nehmen wir die Maßstäbe für unser Handeln und Unterlassen? Wie können wir alle gut auf unserem Planeten Erde leben?

Dieses Buch möchte dazu anregen, sich auch unter ungewohnten Blickwinkeln mit diesen Fragen auseinanderzusetzen. Es ver sammelt Texte führender Forscherinnen und Forscher und engagierter Journalistinnen und Journalisten zu diesen Themen. Auswahlprinzip ist, vielfältige und fundierte Positionen zu zeigen! Zu den Autoren gehören unter anderem Hans Jonas, Giovanni Maio, Jens Reich und E. O. Wilson.

Das Lesebuch „Biologie und Ethik: Leben als Projekt" erscheint zum gleichnamigen hr-iNFO-Funkkolleg und bietet der Leserin und dem Leser anregende Denkanstöße!

Eine inspirierende Lektüre!

Schweizerbart Science Publishers

Johannesstraße 3 A, 70176 Stuttgart, Germany. Tel.: +49 (711)351456-0
Fax: +49 (711)351456-99   order@schweizerbart.de   www.schweizerbart.com

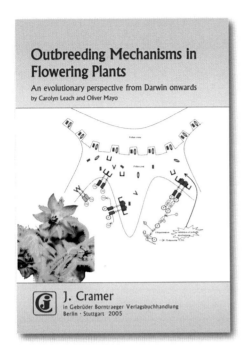

Outbreeding Mechanisms in
Flowering Plants
An evolutionary perspective from Darwin onwards
by Carolyn Leach and Oliver Mayo

J. Cramer
in Gebrüder Borntraeger Verlagsbuchhandlung
Berlin · Stuttgart 2005

Carolyn Leach; Oliver Mayo

Outbreeding Mechanisms in Flowering Plants

An evolutionary perspective from Darwin onwards

2005. VIII, 147 pages, 20 figures, 28 tables, 14 x 21 cm
ISBN 978-3-443-50029-0, paperback, 24.00 €

further information:
www.borntraeger-cramer.de/9783443500290

In this book both the fitness effects of different breeding systems and plant outbreeding mechanisms, in particular self-incompatibility in all its variety, are reviewed for the first time.

The integrating factor is Charles Darwin, who with several Central European scientists initiated the modern investigation of both topics. The historical content is designed to demonstrate the development of understanding, the lineage of concepts and lines of investigation. This presentation of the basic historical background permits the incorporation of many detailed mechanisms into this short book.

The authors have condensed hundreds of references very substantially in order to make clear the strong associations between breeding system and fitness. Particular attention is focussed on major unsolved problems, especially the origin of self-incompatibility and the origin of diversity within these systems.

The envisaged readership encompasses academics, research students (from the end of the first degree upwards) and research workers in the plant sciences.

J. Cramer in **Borntraeger Science Publishers**
Johannesstraße 3A, 70176 Stuttgart, Germany
Tel.: +49 (711)351456-0   Fax: +49 (711)351456-99
order@borntraeger-cramer.com.de   www.borntraeger-cramer.com